YOUTMAN

SATURDAY'S CHILD

Terrence R. E. Burey

YOUTMAN

SATURDAY'S   CHILD

Terrence R. E. Burey

Terrence R. E. Burey

*I dedicate this to my mom and dad, Ivy and Winston Haye,
who are convinced they 'saw something'
long before I made the
first keystroke.*

Terrence R. E. Burey

Growing up in Jamaica, I was exposed to the works of Tennyson, Wordsworth, Robbins and Shakespeare as well as works produced by a few local writers. They lacked the necessary mettle and brought-up-cy to express intrinsic, rural psyche-forming experiences, mannerisms, and attitudes. I aimed at righting the negligence, filling the myopic void, rebalancing the inequities and injustices and repositioning our undocumented life.

The evolutionary style of this manuscript demonstrates the cultural diversity, style and message of the characters. In *Youtman: Saturday's Child,* typical antagonist/protagonist scenarios are absent; instead the characters dictate its style and pace. You will experience subtle cultural clashes and classes/colour conflicts and the innovative essence of the Jamaican Creole as spoken by characters with varying levels of education. Liberties are taken with the traditional English syntax, grammar, and punctuation; it is infused with vernacular that spans the idiosyncratic range of our communication patterns and innuendos.

I use wit and sarcasm in the conversations and I incorporate the plethora of cultural features embedded in our rural way of life – the village concept of nurturing and discipline, our educational system, our religions, our games and burial customs. *Youtman: Saturday's Child* forces readers to re-examine how we managed to survive despite being whipped but not beaten.

Join Ackee Red, Bull, Canepiece Rat, Claude, Dimples, Jack's Hill Daisy, as well as Youtman, and re-live the challenges of the past and the hopes of the future. Be comforted to know that we are a people destined to be great and like *Saturday's Child,* "We have far to go."

Youtman: Saturday's Child is presented by an adult, but is seen through the eyes of a maturing lad.
TREB

ACKNOWLEDGEMENTS

My grandparents have been extremely instrumental in my existence and by extension, the existence of this document; grandmother unwittingly sowed the seed for this passion.

My wife and daughter tolerated my life of coexisting in isolation for six years as I wrote and revised several portions of what follows; for their tolerance, understanding and support I thank them. Dr. Enid Eumina Bogle of Howard University a very special thanks for her insight and patience; for her understanding of the vernacular and the judicious use of her dreaded red pen. My friends who appreciated my candour and recall and suggested that I do this for posterity, I say thanks again. Charmaine Hibbert who knew I had a lot to learn and bought me the green handbook... Bovel Anderson, through thick and thin.... Certainly, Miss Lou's promotion of our culture on a global scale and, in particular, for her prolific use of our Jamaican Creole. And to my friends who hung in there for the long haul, I thank you for being such good sounding boards. Tenk hunnu!!

Terrence R. E. Burey

Copyright © Terrence R. E. Burey 2002

Published by JamRock Publishing Enterprises
P.O. Box 541106
Lake Worth
Florida 33454-1106

ISBN 0-9714795-0-X
First Edition
Printed in the United States of America

BOOKS ARE AVAILABLE AT QUANTITY DISCOUNTS WHEN USED TO PROMOTE PRODUCTS OR SERVICES. FOR INFORMATION PLEASE WRITE TO THE MARKETING DIVISION, JAMROCK PUBLISHING ENTERPRISES, P.O. BOX 541106, LAKE WORTH, FLORIDA, 33454-1106.

Author's Note

Terrence R. E. Burey

Chapter One

SEEKING BETTER LIVES COUNTRY BUMPKINS flood Kingston the capital city. Fresh from parochial school sewing class, many of the young women come job-hunting as seamstresses to the garment industry. When, as is likely, aspirations fall short, some become laundresses, others cooks and baby sitters for our society's landed gentry. Young men in similar plights also arrive close-mindedly astute, geared as prepared, with the syllabus fed education, as gardeners and tradesmen. Their influx stresses the housing industry,

1

transforms single-family homes into weekly-rented, unfurnished, multi-unit tenements. Most arrive almost financially broke and undecided about their future. The generosity of a cousin, friend, or a friend of a friend, pre-empts the preying of many 'unscrewpulous' landlords, with proclivities that infringe on the ethical innocence of the unsuspecting women.

Tenants converge from all over the island. They use cheap fabric to create a sense of privacy in their confining apartments. Their congenial dispositions inspire lasting friendships across termite-laden doorways, on barracks-like verandas, at communal standpipes, in shower-lines or along clotheslines. Their success is shared equitably with family members 'back home' in the 'country'. Settlers on the city's east side fare better than those in the more barracks-like conditions, in the city's near west-side, in Trench Town's Government yards.

The rural lifestyle is perpetuated by the remainder; with attrition, young men settle into predetermined societal roles as farmers while some young women hanker to Higglering, a female-centric occupation: Selling crops in the regional markets to assume a level of financial 'insecurity'. The term Higgler is an acronym: Highly Innovative Go-getter Group Legitimising Entrepreneurship on Roads and Sidewalks. Higglers are from the same Diaspora: Black girls, with excellent scholastic abilities. Derailed. They commute with their produce, on bone-jarring trips under tarpaulins, sitting on anatomically damaging, narrow planks in the backs of wooden bodied trucks along deplorable roads, to markets island-wide; in their parish capitals and Kingston's 'Kerrnatian' Market. They convey updates both ways: news of progressive rural events as well as gossip-detailing dalliances involving the rent collectors. They also bring money from prospering migrants to relatives 'back a country'.

By day, many transplanted city slickers pound the pavement, job-hunting; at night, they feign sleep so the extended host family can tend to personal matters.

*   *   *

A typical socialite, Moravia Grantham, a woman of European descent with similar paternal and maternal genetics, lives in elite Jacks Hill; she hires Daisy, a conscientious resident of this tenement as a baby-sitter. Daisy is the fifth of seven siblings; she makes a stellar attempt at avoiding the dead-end trail in Free Hill, Saint Mary. Twenty-two miles 'as the crow flies' equates to thirty-five, time-consuming, erosion-prone, serpentine miles of an obstacle course, which include a compulsory stop at West Street then a walk to Parade for connections to Barbican then finally to Jacks Hill.

At seventeen, she's a year advanced in her curriculum and graduates at the top of her class. She aspires to be a teacher and stop the cycle of her farming brothers and higglering sisters. She lacks the financial backitive to realise her dream but remains optimistic. To attend school she must ford Woman River, morning and evening, and the severe terrain causes her to maintain a terse physique as is evidenced by her sculpted calves. She negotiates precarious tracks for a mile and a half between her home and the main road's conglomerate compaction of clay and river stones barefooted because her parents can barely afford shoes and it's only after fording the river that she washes her feet and wears her only pair of shoes, the remainder of the way, to school.

She envisions her baby-sitting workdays as being spent in 'Eaven down low: The smoke-free kitchen where she fixes the miracle baby's meals contain kerosene appliances: a stove, refrigerator as well as running water. She rationalizes: An all-powerful God must love smoke because, "'E allows it to rise." Daisy's gift is to absorb and repeat conversations verbatim.

Optimistic; she converses with obliging, successful-looking individuals who seem capable of helping her gain acceptance in a teachers college. She utilizes her one weekend off per month to window shop among the elite along King Street on Saturdays then worships in church on Sundays. She shares anecdotal work experiences with her fellow tenants in comedic sessions.

*   *   *

My grandfather did a stint in Cuba as a tailor, returns to the island but shuns rural Clarendon's predominant wattle houses, full of vents and chooses Kingston's tenements. Working at 32 Luke Lane he acquires the pseudonym, Tailor Willie. He sends for Iris his wife and Jasmine their daughter. His strong work ethics and meticulous attention to details are commanding an expanding clientele. They settle at Daisy's digs: 40 Johns Lane and embark on their tradition as lovers of children, adopt light-skinned Dahlia who resembles my grandmother more than Jasmine does. They share the single family, four-bedroom/living and dining rooms tenement residence with: Fitzy and Blossom from Bog Hole, Percy of Petersfield and Rosie (also known as 'Toe Nail' because she likes to paint 'them' with annatto seeds) of Hertford, Leonard and Clover from Crofts Hill as well as Free Hill Claude -- Daisy's cousin. All the rooms multiplex as bed, living, dining and bathrooms. The cramped kitchen accommodates both the inept men and the expert women capable of making a five-course meal with little more than a dash of fine salt. The men who fend for themselves in their job-necessitated sweethearts absence foster cooking/compensation arrangements with the women there. Citified residents now, they change their rural, Wednesday/washday riverside commiserating for Saturday/cistern gossip.

* * *

The women, inculcate good family values in the children, indoctrinate and ensure that we maintain good Church habits, take us, children, grandchildren and/or adoptions alike to Sunday school and Church services with the proviso: a place at the right hand of The Master waits in the hereafter. Teenage girls become heads of households. Men are the leaders of communities and the nation, but the adage: Behind every man is a good woman, holds true. Even when there's a father figure present in a household, it is still the women who inculcate good family values in us.

Most men worship other beings than The Holy Trinity. Some choose the Rum Bars' spirit in the bottle served at room temperature, others the four-legged racers via the Off Track betting spots and still others rendezvous with both the jockey and the beast every Saturday, post time, at the track, until they answer calls to a one-on-one with The Maker.

* * *

Across the river, thirteen-year-old Pansy, Miss Pinnie's second daughter's spirituality, breeds pregnancy avoidance. It's summer. It's Wednesday. It's washday.

"Pansy!"

"Yes Mama."

"Yu one have fe go river go wash today… "

"Why Ivy can't come too Mama?"

"Me need her help."

"A wha' de matter Mama?"

"A nutting much me chile, just gas."

"But wi just drink tea Mama…"

"De breakfus cause de ly gas, me soon feel better." She winces, but the hides the painful expression.

"Yu awright Mama?"

"Yes me chile!" She fibs. "Ivy oh!"

Singing sanctimoniously the call is unheard. In the chorus, "Then sings my soul," she gets to "How great Thou art!" Who pops into her mind? Superman. Smirking she mumbles: "Boy, the devil strong sah."

Her mother's third call registers.

She runs outside to respond: "Yes Mama!"

"Gal… yu know from when me a call yu?"

She responds with downcast eyes: "Me did a sing mam… sorry." Then she observes her mother's sweating: "Mama yu no look good?"

"Pickney, me jus a kin teet fe cover heartburn."

"Yu alright though Mama?"

"Yes. Pansy!"

"Yes Mama!"

"Boil lilly ginger tea fe me before the fire ded."

* * *

Following Friday night cycle sports 'show cut': the open-air movie theatres close. Tonight and Saturday night, revellers converge and newly formed alliances blossom into covert dalliances. Couples frolic, saunter through Parade, up and down King Street, sashay along Harbour Street out to Rae Town and back, till the wee hours. Male vendors roam the city behind pushcarts, some with steam whistling through contraptions strapped to their bicycles' carriers, others ride atop mule and donkey drawn carriages while enterprising females sell foodstuff they prepare from stationary glass-cases. They noisily announce their wares:

"Booby egg!"

"Coconut drops!"

"Fudge!"

"Icicles!"

"Peanut!"

"Cashew!"

"Ice-cream!"

"Cocanaat!"

Those who can't buy sponge on the better off, asking,

"Beg yu piece nuh?" Or settle for the leftovers later, when they get home. Under the streetlight, some cotching residents lollygag until households retire. Only then they can spread 'beds' in common areas.

Meagre dogs bark incessantly at Layban, a cat that scampered up an ackee tree next door.

Daisy, home for the weekend, must share a home with another set of strangers. She is adjusting to intimate relations by which she has been blindsided, relations with the compliments of her single-bed partner, Free Hill Claude, her contact on arrival as a country bumpkin. He was carpenter in the city while was still a student. He leaves the group on the veranda and retires to their makeshift bedroom; just beyond the former living room entrance where the translucent smoked-glass insets in the French door emit filtered streetlight into their room and its sunburst-patterned transom shadows strafe the warped, soot-covered ceiling.
Decision time: "Daisy, no bother keep up the people dem too late, a dem market day tomorrow."

"Lawd Claude, you see anybody yawning? Go eat the Julie Mango me bring fe yu."
Rosie the coolie: "Missis, a no we him a worry bout and the uptown mango can't satisfy the need him feel."
She hisses her teeth: "Well since you know so much tell me is who or what 'im a worry bout?"

Tight quarters afford Rosie the luxury of speaking from experience: "Yu know what me mean! When yu turn een, things change."

"But Rosie! What are you talking about?"

"Yu forget! Is a sheet separate we bedroom!"

Leonard: "Hey Claude! Me catch de horse yu know."

"Yu mean the one in the third race?"

"The same one… him win!"

"Good ciga'! Den yu naw buy me one beer?"

"We can go knock one down a Missa Cox yes."

Claude rejoins Daisy's group delivery on the lifestyle of the rich and 'infamous': "…the amount leftover from them Wednesday night party! …Me telling yu it could feed we tea lunch and dinner!"

Leonard: "Then why yu never bring some home man?"

"Yu too negrish! Me say Wednesday. It stale."

"Negrish mi eye. Dinna an breakfast and lunch."

Curious Dahlia: "So stale! Wha kind of party she have?"

"Sixteenth birthday party for har fresh son!"

Rosie: "Him still a touch touch yu?" Daisy glances up and Leonard pipes in: "Daisy… Me couldn't keep it, a me tell Rosie him, but what we going to do? It rampant!"

Claude: "A hear, but a waitin on yu to tell me."

Daisy: "Cho, a box way the boy han."

It has escalated beyond that though; she has had to give in; he threatened to tell mother his lunch was unsatisfactory again; Daisy remembers only too well the ultimatum Miss Moravia gave her: "Girl. Make Master Wally unhappy again, in any way shape or form, I am dismissing you!"

That night Wallingford came into her bedroom; he put his hand over her mouth, startled her, but she conscientiously offered no resistance. She lay motionless while he did his unprotected business. Her recourse: I guess a have to make double sure nutten no happen.... A 'ave to drink some soap water and take one headache pill and aerated water tomorrow.... And sighs.

Rosie knows more: "So Daisy! What really a gwaan in high society girl? Tell me nuh."

"Me dear! Master Wally going study fe lawyer." Leonard: "You know, when me was fe him age, not one so so God body in the whole district could tell me how to turn Barrister. You think a little ask me ask!"

Claude: "You know bout barrister inna fe yu bush?"

Clover: "Pastor nor head teecha couldn't tell you?"

Leonard: "Yu ask it like joke..."

Clover: "A no joke me a mek, tradition me talkin bout!"

Leonard: "Head teecha know and wouldn't tell me."

"Him never know a ting," said Daisy, adding, "My missus friend tell Wally fe learn fe fly plane!"

Leonard: "And dem only teach we fe use machete."

Claude changes the subject: "Leonard!"

"Yes me fren."

"This chattin chattin make me throat dry man."

"A get the message…. Yu ready fe beer sah?"

And adds: "A wi bring back a stout Clover."

* * *

Parson after church: "Sister D! A word with you…"

"Yes Pastor."

"How you like the service."

"Good pastor."

"A have to run but… mek a get to the point…"

"Yes pastor."

"You throw good collection."

"A short dem pickney lunch money sometime."

"The Lord bless you… dem wi live, trust Him."

"Pastor little fasting never kill Jesus…"

"Amen sister."

"So wat de matter pastor? Me do sumting rong?"

Smirking: "No no. As yu know me gardener dead sudden. Sen yu big son come work down at the manse."

"Massa Gad bless yu Pastor and de five mile won't kill the boy pastor."

"He might see The Light, comb him head."

"A walk wid him eye dem red, bout him dred."

"What him name again?"

"Tat, pastor."

"The yard want to weed bad."

"A wi have him dere a mawnin pastor.... Is wat doctor inques say kill him pastor?"

"Heat stroke me dear sista... heat stroke..."
She walks home with a single mindset, disinterested in the banter about The Message's interpretation. She attends to the pressing matter before undressing: "Boy! Yu a come out ya go work... God bless pastor him tek pity pon you, gi'e yu jab down a him yard."

"I man naw trod six mile afta no false prophet."

"A five mile and if yu nuh go yu naw tan ya!"

"Whe I fe go?"

"Me nuh care... me an yu Pupa try..."

"No worry bout I. Jah won't forsake I.... Seen."

"Me nuh know wha we fe do wid yu."

"We! We is weeble. Get conscious. Say I an I."

"Me naa tek up yu foolishness"

"Foolinish a de gaabage down a church!"

"If yu waan swalla food in ya yu betta go wuk!"

"I man no walla walla inna foolinish eyrilize dat!"

"Eyralize! But a wha dis pon me. Wha it mean?"

"Wat de pork heart parson dem call realize!"

"Leff me Gad and me pahsen outa yu foolinish."

"A full time consciousness reach church peeple."

"Me dun chat, if yu no tek the job jus leff ya."

"Wen madda forsake I, Jah wi tek I up."

"Tek yu dutty bundle an go live wid yu Jah."

"I an I live wid Jah in I an I heart."

"Well crawl up een deh wid Him, come out yah!"

"Cool nuh Mama man, yu nuh haffy fuss nuh more! I wi go show de preacher man de light."

"Yu backle light?"

"Naw, said light fe stop him from walk round blind, like Barthemeus."

"Go wash yu smelly dutty seff fe de jab."

"See all dat. Call I unclean!"

"Yes."

"I an I Faadah wi tek I an I said way. Said speed. I can't fahsake I an I Faadah I man done kno…"

* * *

They return from Missa Cox's bar a few hours later. The residents are gone to bed. Whispering, inebriated Claude inquires: "Daisy! Yu a sleep?"

"No."

"Turn round face me den…. We need to talk."

"'Bout wat now man!"

"Well… we situation."

"Wat you mean?"

"Yu can stay 'ere as long as yu want yu know."

"We agree on dat soon as me get off the bus."

"Yu can pitch een in any way yu want… "

"Me know… by the way…"

"Gwaan talk me 'earing yu."

14

"'Ow you just introduce introduce me as Daisy!"

"Then nuh so yu name!"

"Yes but you always call me Cousin Daisy!"

He chuckles audibly but it is imperceptible from the other side of the makeshift wall. Now belly to belly he touches the thin sheet over her toes with his: "A t'ink we should keep it between us." Single bed privileges places him just a heartbeat away. They sense each other's thrumming heartbeat and breathe in each other's faces heavily now.

She thinks long and hard before answering: "Claude…a think yu drunk, but member dis still, I didn't leave me yard to come turn nobody sweet 'art… a could 'ave stayed right in Free Hill and do that… me 'ave hambition…" She pulls her toes away and continues: "Me want to make something of meself… so if all you lookin' is a sweet 'art then me might as well get up now and pack me grip, me never take that much of me ketteh-ketteh out a it yet anyway."

"Shh shh! No man, mine yu wake everybody." He pulls back his toes though they are only caressing air then continues: "Me only feel sweet is all. Not because but still for all, me will still feel for yu in me heart. We need to talk so we know what to hexpec."

"Well start with wat you hexpec from me?"

"Make me start wid what me don't hexpect!"

"Start anywhere yu like."

"Me don't hexpect you to stay 'ere turn wutliss."

"No!"

"That never in my plans!"

"Well me plan to put me self through school"

"A admire yu ambition."

"A going to tell you something..."

"Awright! Awright! Me a listen."

"Me starting to depend on yu, yu kno!"

"A true Daze… me never know."

"A true."

Their toes find each other's again, sans the sheet and Daisy responds: "At work! A think bout yu every day."

"Me tink bout yu day and night."

"You kno what me a consider?"

"No! Tell me nuh …"

"Country people…bredda and sister pickney…"

His fingers find hers in the darkness.

Meanwhile in the original master bedroom, their voices a mere whisper…

"Willie yu a sleep?"

"No, what happen."

"I don't like to encourage yu gambling but…"

"But what…"

"I see the numbers man, a ask him what play…"

"What him say play?"

"Sixteen."

"Sixteen?"

"What a way it get yu excited? Yu win?"

"No… is not fe meself."

"Den is who?"

"…Fitzy! Fitzy!"

"Mine yu wake up the whole house!"

"Wake wha? De peeple dem a sleep?"

"Matters not man… why yu so loud?"

"Loud me eye… it important!"

"More than last week?"

"Yes man, is him tramcar fare him bet!"

"Me have something else to talk to you 'bout."

"A what now Iris?"

"Fe mek ends meet me going to start sew."

"But you a sew a' ready."

"Sew to sell me mean."

"Sell where?"

"Me hear Morant Bay doing good business…"

He hears her but his mind is racing, freedom a few
nights a week: "So when you would go Dawlin?"

"What a way you get sweet!"

"Sweet wha, all me do is ask you a question."

"Yes but you a call me darling same time!"

"Is not the first!"

"No, but the last was a long time ago…"

"GoodGadaheavenmissis!"

"No badda call down God, you nuh know Him."

"You say Him died for me and you." His mind on Clover: "When you going to Morant Bay?"

"Me thinking bout weekend time."
Freedom! "From when till when?"

"You have plenty time to worship the horses."

"Honestly, racing is far far from my mind."

"You and Ginger from up the lane and the constant drinkin... me concerned bout the girls."

"No worry man, I will watch out for them!"
She ignores his sincere-sounding reply: "So good Dahlia and Jasmine big enough to take care of themselves."

"Dat not necessary. I am right here."

"Just the same. Them big. And me haffy worry."

"So what kind of things you going to sell?"

"Children's clothes... special orders for women."

"You carry book fe tek measurement?"

"Remember me can make it out of me head!"

"But you bad Iris!"

"Me no bad, me good."

"Is the slang Iris."

"Me not into them worlean things, Willie!"

A Clover me hear with it: he thinks to himself.

Chapter Two

MISS PINNIE DISMISSES PANSY TO THE RIVER
"'Member...Don't mek no boy pickney touch touch
yu!" Ivy resumes her chores and will leave for the
field soon. She finishes her tea and retires. Lying there
reality sets in, she muses: "All the same, if anything
happen to me, me two girls them pass the worse...
them have ambition, me nothing but a higgler... that's
all the business dealin Buckra Massa provide fe we
poor people... but them can dream, it free.... While
there is life there is hope... me only pray God the

ginger tea help me." She soon falls asleep because like the boiled herbal remedies that Miss Ida concocts from various shrubs, roots, barks and leaves, this one cures her illnesses. Few people will see doctor at clinic or hospital and fewer still will find their way to the out-of-town Bush Doctor, flying his white flag, high on the bamboo pole.

* * *

Eighteen-year-old Frankie, Mango to his friends because, as his only true vice, he habitually steals any and all of said fruit they possess, is cogitating other light-fingered habits. Man-o-yard since his stepfather who never bothered to discuss his near-constant migraine headaches died three years ago of a brain aneurysm, does as he pleases. His fifteen-year-old colour-centric named brother, Blackman is blindsided. Following a breakfast of calalloo with a hint of salt fish and fried dumpling and bush tea, he pats his mother on her shoulder, his brother on his head and without the use of either arm, pushes his chair back, stands and announces, "Mama me no de ya now ma. Blackman wi tie out the goat."

His brother's eyes proffer rejection but it is his slow-eating mother with the mouthful who speaks, "Wha yu mean eh!"

"Me ha sittn fe do mah." Trails his exit.

"You can say that again sah... a jus' today me and Fitzy a say that once we finish paint them is the last time we can set foot them. Go back there after rich peeple move een and them bawl out, thief."

"That don't have to be so you know me boy."

"Heh! How we going see the inside again?"

"Buy it!"

"Ha ha Missa Cox, how me going do that?"

"See Fitzy here ask him."

"Eveling, eveling... ask me what."

"Evening Fitzy... a just telling your partner that him should buy one of the houses up at Waltham Park!"

Percy: "A jus finish laugh. Missa Cox a mad Super."

"Listen. This is a man with nough experience."

"What kind of experience you have Missa Cox?"

His slight olive skin, laced with freckles suddenly looks alive. He covers his thin lips with his left index finger and places the thumb on his left jaw. He blinks rapidly then sighs: "See, I am a man of two spirits, Percy."

"What you mean by that sah?"

"Super here was a gardener at the seminary."

"Seminary sah?"

"Yes, studying to become a man of the cloth."

"What him mean Super?"

"Missa Cox was going to be a parson."

"Then a which crosses stop you Missa Cox?"

23

"Got disenchanted with the whole affair my boy."
It's over Percy's head but he aspires towards conversational enlightenment: "I see, set up Super wid a liquor fe me sar."

"Sure my boy…. The regular?"

"Yes sah!" Comes as an anxious reply from Super.

Percy digresses: "Super what take you so long man… yu know me could have finish me drink a'ready!"

"Not when yu buying… the way yu sip sip?"

"Me jus like nurse liquor, a Missa Cox buy dis."

"Right Nurse… a you that from now… 'Nurse'"

"I second that Super… Nurse!"

"Me not paying yu bad mind. So wat keep yu?"

"A talk to a man bout a one day roas'…"

"A little race horse money eenh Super."

"Right Nurse."

Missa Cox burst out: "Nurse! Ha ha ha ha ha ha."

Percy ignores the name, hopes it works: "Missa Cox!"

"Here Super …yes my boy a hearing you."

"Something on my mind a need help with sar."

"Ask away my boy… anytime…"

"Yes sah."

"I might surprise you what a know my boy…"

"A already surprise sah… yu a train fe parson…"

"I prefer it said my way my boy…"

Nurse: "Exchange one spirit for another sah, a remember."

Taking a sip: "Presactly. My boy what's your question."

"Dem couldn' find African histry fe teach we?"

"My boy drink up, drink up."

"Why sar?"

"A buying you another one."

"Why sar?"

Nurse chimes in: "Percy you fool fool... man a buy you a drink! Don't cross question him, empty de glass!"

Percy's empty glass hit the linoleum-covered countertop before Fitzy finished speaking: "Pour yourself a drink my boy, it's going to be a long evening."

Percy complies, now he's able to take bigger sips.

Missa Cox goes through his meditation ritual; clears his throat and looks out onto Rum Lane's congregation, at the scurrying children and passing pedestrian parents and young adults. He massages his palms together and begins: "You know my boy... when I studied as a man of the cloth that was most haunting... I asked... none of my superiors cared to answer... I persisted my boy... but their answer was unsatisfactory ...other people struggled with this question before... what I found... is that... since our migration.... Young bloods like you... only learn African culture and history... absorbing tales from your elders, stories that must be remembered my boy... and passed on in like manner... undocumented."

"By what sah?"

"Word of mouth my boy; each one tell one, this is our only means of relaying the tradition. Yet my boy, simple efforts to perpetuate our history through the verbal was thwarted, because our conversing affects the process we were brought here for." He pauses for effect. Takes a sip then continues, "To break our backs working for them. Whenever we stop work to talk they try to deny us the opportunity to gather and chat, deny this simple act my boy. It's hard, not hard; it's impossible to know presactly what the founding fathers told the next generation. Likewise it is hard to know what they passed on. Why is that you might ask?"

"Is exactly that me wondering sah."

"I'm glad you ask. Whenever someone else relays the story, something gets lost in the translation."

"A suh nuh sah?"

"Back then Africans couldn't write, still can't, in appreciable numbers... are the most illiterate in the..." Enthused, Percy cuts Missa Cox off and interjects: "But Missa Cox, you don't look African sah!"

"I'll pardon you interruptions when they are relevant to the subject, when they are germane... but you shouldn't interrupt me...or anyone teaching you

something... not a good practice my boy... not good."
Both Nurse and Super want to audibly concur with the
bit of advice but they decline as a matter of respect.

"I am of mixed blood my boy... just like you..."

"Me mixed sah?"

"Doing it again my boy!"

Fitzy proffers an apology: "No pay the boy bad mind
sah. Him no have no brought-up-see..."

Looking sternly at Percy he continues: "I am a typical
point five mix. African woman and the Scottish white
man... slave in me... when I go to 'Merica or England,
white man sees no difference between you and me...
we're both black men in his eyes."

It's Fitzy's turn to interrupt: "A true sah!"

"Yes my boy."

"A can't believe what a hearin wid me own ears."

"Believe it my boy, believe it. We need to use
our heads for more than a resting place for heavy loads.
We are the most illiterate in the Caribbean you know!
We need to start expanding our minds. Do it so that we
will be able us to pick sense out o nonsense. Follow
their speeches and ploys in clear and understanding
manners. Follow their empty promises... the false
hopes that our leaders, like knotted jackass rope dangle
like mental bangle from pulpit, podium, rostrum,
emporium, shop piazza, truck back and over radio."

Fitzy: "Yu miss yu calling sah, shoulda tu'n preacher."
He considers it a relevant interruption: "Who'd minister to people like you? Because you don't go to church."

"Yu have a point there sah… yu have a point."

"Let me finish…. Shamefully, we stand at the propaganda receiving end and thanks to illiteracy, grasp one percent of what they spew at us…"
Fitzy: "A true sah… a true!"

"A know it my boy… and, with smiles wider than the little unpaved dusty tracks they pass off as country roads, we listen to their entire message, hearing all but understanding none, with glazed eyes, pick up every tenth word and understand every twentieth. They don't have so much tings to say anyway so luckily they repeat themselves. … we pick up two to three percent, go off feeling wonderful and smug, we get the gist…. They don't even disguise the malarkey because of our pitiful inability to see through plain and simple lie." He pauses to take a sip and it only now that Nurse and Super can touch theirs. It is only now that he realises that Claude and Leonard, going along Laws Street on their way home, on recognizing their tenement yard family, joined the lesson in progress.
Leonard chimes in: "A gospel truth yu a talk sah. Sorry fe interrup sah, but beg yu serve we a drink before you get back inna the conscious haggiment though…"

Percy: "A barefoot white rum, him no have no ice!"
Claude ribs him: "But hear country come a town!"
Fitzy: "Nurse shet up mek the man finish talk."
Claude: "Nurse! A how that name come 'bout Super?"
In deference to Missa Cox Fitzy cuts it short: "We can cover that later, gwaan with what yu sayin' Missa Cox!"

"Very well then my boy… as I was saying… we need to make it fashionable to go to adult literacy classes…so that as the majority of the society we can take our rightful place as leaders and rulers in it. But we have to creep before we walk, so in the immediate future, the thing it will do for us is make we understand what going on, especially, especially when they make empty promises about the one hundred menial jobs they will provide in an area with the three thousand unemployed casual labourers, we will be literate enough to rebuff the crap! Logically follow… see if what they tell us is what they print in the newspaper; challenge the inconsistencies and inaccuracies; not because some juvenile read the paper aloud for us but because our gut check plus the reality of what is said and what we read in print either add up or don't add up. More likely than not it will be the latter so rightly, on that matter, we can create a kerfuffle. Through education, we'll refute the crap. The fact of the matter is that the sooner we can bring things to that end the better!"

Percy applauds Missa Cox's eloquence and verbalizes: "Missa Cox…a get a education this evening, it rival any parochial school back a country… a apologise for interrupting yu so much sah… a appreciate this a lot sah… and a going to take yu up on yu offer, anytime a have any questions… a know whey to come sah… serve one more round and put it on me bill till tomorrow Friday sah, a have to buy yu a drink sah."

"Apology accepted my boy. But you don't have to buy me one you know. But I don't turn down liquor or money, let alone both o them same time my boy."

They all burst out laughing.

* * *

Tat, on the job a week, is weeding around some Crotons under a window when he overhears this conversation:

"A wonder if you can answer few question."

"Glad to help deacon. Anything in particular?"

"As a matter of fact there is pastor."

"Well as they say: Sock it to me, heh heh."

"Pastor, we are staunch in our belief in This Holy Ghost but we are cautioned against extending that belief into other ghosts or duppies! Ghost is ghost, yu agree right pastor?"

"In the African villages they used to fear ghosts."

"So the Ghost only there to keep us in check?"

"Oh no. To keep fresh white is right. That's why a white Jesus is on most calendars every year!"

"Why they allow Emancipation Day?"

"Celebrate Emancipation Day, oppression 'n suppression return that same nite, backs continue to break and ache fo Buckra Massas' sake, nothing change, nothing strange."

"Right pastor... them talkin 'bout independence."

"Independence from man not God!"

"Independence can wash way religion pastor?"

"They seek independence as beings in destiny."

"But is not they pastor, is we..."

"No deacon, they won't learn, we seek education, and we decide what to tell them." He continues: "It's a little known fact locally, but on every continent people worship at least one different God. It's unclear how many different gods we, as humanity really serve; but it's a fair bet that from Australia's Aborigines to Africa's Zulus, there are enough Gods to fill a very big Church. Winchester Cathedral comes to mind. Mankind fights over religious beliefs, more than anything else, more than it fights over everything else combined. Based on their sizes we even have categories and sub-categories for most of them. Congregations fight over Religions, Sects over their Cults, others The Occults and the last their Skulduggery. At

Terrence R. E. Burey

different times, different nations, at the top of their game become The World Super Power. Tribes, as they like to refer to your progenitors in The Mother-land, don't get to play in this stratospheric game. Challengers pray their God grant them perfect aim, so that their weaponry overpower The Big Dog's soldiers, to win the top slot. Like in all other nations, we go off to World War, war in the east, war in the west, fight because the leaders say we should, the carnage and a grief-stricken mourning, the number of relatives left asking the rhetorical why, why, why is the common refrain. I have a big hang-up with constantly answering this question; it is usually posed to me because I've been to divinity school. I am forced to maintain a certain degree of faience, faithism and stoicism and justify why such and such a youtman has to catch a bullet with his brain, a big heavy bomb on some distant land. You wouldn't know how many times I am tempted to have a heart to heart with bereaved souls and segue into this... 'You boy never have no need to go a war and die... If the two leaders go settle the crap instead of sending everybody else's loved ones... make that loved ones from the poorer class... you, my collection givers, the crap could be settled with far less bloodshed, carnage, grief, burial, orphaning, widowing, cemetery over-filling, covertly stacked burying, grave robbing, cement engraving and grieving.'

"That's true pastor. That's very, very true. A did say is two question but a have another question?"

"Fire away man… all is fair in love and war."

"Who or what is God pastor?"

"He can be anything. A Stone, Rat, any Bird, Alligator, Snake, Cow…before we even begin to get close to The Trinity; The Father, The Son and The Holy Ghost which as we discuss includes a ghost. We have Yahweh, Allah and at least one other dead man than Jesus, Jah Haille Selassie I, whom the Rastafarian people, not cult, using our King James Version of The Holy Bible, can prove is a direct descendant of King Solomon. Time and again, it has been argued rather vociferously, by The Jamaican Rastaman like me gardener Tat outside, that, 'Selassie can't dead.'"

"A whay yu say... yu gardener is a dread?"

"Me dear sah instead o the boy emulate him madda, boy mek weed fly up inna him head."

"At least him conscious enough fe know that man can worship other gods."

"Sound like yu want quit what we have here and go join him?"

"No. But most of us will die ignorant of that."

"So it go me brother. But in doing our thing hopefully one and two will pick up something from it."

"Then you can't make a more concerted effort for that to happen pastor?"

"What you want man? Me work myself out of a job?"

"A job is all it is pastor?"

"Change the subject. How things in the district?"

"The members go a property every day, Friday when them get pay, them pay off the various bill and basically carry the rest come gi'e yu Sunday!"

"Good, as you know the more the merrier."

"But we not convincing too many men pastor!"

"I only see them wartime, funeral and wedding."

"Come straighten up them soul…"

"Yea. The medical profession have it to say is them… what the devil is that word Dear God."

"Testosterone?"

"Thanks! How you know that word anyway?"

"District nurse, we talk from time to time."

"She tell you because yours get high with her?"

"Well you know we are all mortal man…"

"Yes brother… is this high level of testosterone in us men that cause us to be such warmongers…"

"Well pastor, short of castration! A wish they could find a way rid us of some, because we don't need the war."

"Amen brother!"

"But we can depend on the women!"

"Amen brother… they are something…"

"Why is that though pastor?"

"Well, you see for yourself… they always come to church… always testifying how they accept Him as Lord and Saviour…give open testimony how He gives them peace… the opposite of war my brother…"

"Pastor, true… peace is the opposite of war…"

"They declare they dying to meet him…but when sickness or old age comes calling, they willing to sell everything and borrow up to their gills…when prayer alone fail they either give it all to the medical doctor or the bush doctor in a last ditch effort to stave off death. Stayin here, before going to the better place they sing, preach, teach, pray dream and lust for."

"And you complaining pastor, just plan them funeral service… sooner or later you will give the speech… in the mean time, collect you collection and preach…"

"Deacon, how them say you no have no sense!"

"Another thing pastor explain to me… 'Some

35

where beyond the blue where there is a mansion for you....' Which blue? What blue? What is blue?"

"Heh eh heh heh heh, noooo.... It's a long story."

"When you fly in a plane the sky move back?"

"That's the heavens declaring the glory of God and the firmament showing his handy work...! Now you won't know this... but I speak from always notice it... up to the last time that the missis and I were takin the children on vacation...flying to 'Merica you know!"

"So how yu explain it parson?"

"Somebody another say a pilot tell him that is a Space Flight Phenomenon! Yu get used to it once yu fly a lot like me... especially in the daytime. Window seat if you please..."

"Well a guess me won't lucky nuff?"

"Well brother, you all pay for all our vacations so the least I can do is share our experience with you."

"Yes pastor... them no sell souvenir a foreign?"

"Yes deacon... yes, all sorts of things!"

"And them sell common pin too?"

"Now come deacon... I get you point but I would have to bring for all four of my congregations..."

"Yes pastor... everybody give collection..."

* * *

They are enjoying a rarity: a private tenement moment.
Sitting on the veranda: "Willie."

"Yes Iris."

"No just siddung so… hold me hand nuh man."

"Wait till we come off of the veranda Iris?"

"People a pass, plenty of them a hold hands."

"Me not out here to watch people, me just a
relax… wait, no Fitzy that a stagger through the gate!"

"A think yu naw watch people?"

"Fitzy a no people! Fitzy a me friend. Fitzy oh!"

"Yes Tailor… eveling Miss Iris!"

"Man yu under two waters!"

"We stop down a Missa Cox and knock one."

"Yu couldn't send call me man?"

"Pcho. From up at Rum Lane and Laws Street
man! But yu nice though Willie!"

"Wha' yu mean?"

"A hold wifey hand and everyting?"

She clutches his hand, as he is about to pull it away.
He relaxes: "Yu no know… fo betta fo worse…"

"Yu definitely have it fo the better me friend."

"Fitzy you are such a gentleman."

"A the truth Miss Iris… me friend know it too…"

"…If yu say so…she no bad."

"Aaahh Willie, that is so nice!"

"Mind yu make anybody hear yu."

"Hi a me Rosie, me is already a witness."

"Pickney shet up yu trap. We is not yu quabbs. Jump in Percy argument no this!" Fitzy adds: "A going let yu ol man Percy put yu in yu bloomin place."

"Excuse me everybody, it won't happen again." Aunt Iris: "In my country we have a saying."

"Yes maam. What it say maam?"

"Little children should be seen and not heard."

"Yes maam."

"And you are not even being seen."

"Yes maam."

"So Fitzy you buy yu drop-han yet?"

"Cho no sah Tailor… me no feel fe no puttykilla number."

"It will hurt you to say particular Fitzy?"

"No maam."

"Well try it sometime man…. you might like it."

"Alright Aunt."

"Giv it a ress Iris… me an de man a talk."

"Whatever you say Willie."

"Dream see dead last night Fitzy, me want buy three."

"Put if a even thrupance pon the three; fe dead… and even a smalls pon thirteen… man yu can't lose!"

Chapter Three

BASIC EDUCATION IS STILL AN ELUSIVE process for the masses. Domestic racism's subtle barriers are slowly eroding. Societal perks work in cryptic ways. We don't see the advertisements in the newspaper inviting credit worthy individuals to enter banks and leave with loans. But, 'those in the know,' get them, to buy the farm, equipment, and any number of things. Education beyond the parochial level is still restricted to the elite. My father experiences this.

*   *   *

Mango squeezes her shoulder: "Wha yu say!" The nearside of her body goes weak; almost drops the wash pan of dirty clothes. She sidesteps to regain her balance and he stays with her, lockstep. Her mind races: Me better tell him fe take off him hand... but... it feel good. Her sister is expected momentarily, she wonders as to his real agenda: "Wha yu a do up here Frankie?" Glibly falling off his tongue: "Nuh you me come check!" He adds, "Come see f yu wan me carry yu wash pan!" She backs up: "No touch me pan."

He asks: "Wha mek?"

She's onto to his game: "You too lie!" He's dumbfounded. She ponders the meaning of his silence: Him not listenin to me him mind on other things: "Me say you too lie."

"Bout wha?"

"Bout say a me yu come check!"

"Why yu say dat?"

"De first me one a go a river, how you know..." He tilts the wash pan; disrupts her train of thought then changes his story: "Me never say me know yu a go a river."

"Yes! A so yu say."

"Cho, a joke me a joke with yu man."

"If yu say so... but don't is Jericho yu live?"

"But yu know whole heap bout me?"

40

"So a lost you lost or a lucky me lucky so?"

"Naw man! Check me come check you man…"

"A how me lucky so?"

"Some girls have all the luck, yu kno!"

"Yu falla dem odder girls go a river too?"

"Them no pretty like you."

He lifts the laundry off her head and swings it under his arm. He clasps her left hand in his now unoccupied right. Looking in her shifting eyes he offers this line: "A long time me a check fe yu you kno!"

"From me a nine and yu a fourteen."

"Bother! Me wouldn't call it that."

"What yu call it? Infant Killa!"

"Naw man, yu mature fast! Yu not no infant!"

"Yu should be shame of yuself…"

"Naw man! Look how long me wait."

"A because me stan-up pon me foot."

"Wha you mean by that?"

"Me wouldn't stand still before now."

"So what this mean. You ready?"

*   *   *

Iris's boost to the family's income effects a move to more spacious tenement digs at 44 Rosemary Lane. Tailor Willie's dalliances continue. The unilateral thorn in Iris's side relocates also. Five families share two bathrooms instead of one and there is a standpipe with cistern in the yard where the laundry can be done at leisure without stooping eternally like at the old one.

Paternally, my Jamaican heritage begins when my grandfather and his brother hightail it in a low-slung canoe from French 'owned' Martinique. On my mother's side, German Jews got in the mix three generations ago. It's while living here that my paternal aunt Fern relocates from Saint Ann. Her youngest brother, Canaan Hill Derrick comes to spend holidays and later move in with dreams of attending Hope College, the most prestigious secondary school island wide. The lowliest caste proles they allow to hob-knob with the gentry are boys of Chinese descent. Even with my father's brilliance he does not pass muster because as the principal likes to say during the invocation: "I personally went over your applications…" and he knows the caste, calibre and addresses of students he prefers. Charity High School suffices.

His excellent math skills cause Mama to solicit his help: "Derrick, help Jasmine with her arithmetic me son, a beg yu… she have plans to advance herself past dressmaking… do nursing." He assumes spying responsibilities, reports to Mama when she speaks to anyone of the opposite sex. The only thing that goes unreported is her dedicated singing on the choir at the Baptist Church. She is an ardent church goer, prays on bended knees, he preys unbending pleas. 'An ounce of prevention is better than a pound of cure' and in that light Iris, assigns Dahlia as Jasmine's bodyguard. For my father-to-be to teach her mathematics his way, he must create a diversion for Dahlia.

"You know… Dahlia! I've been thinking…"

"O' oh… no you don't…not me too…"

"No man, no man… hear me out…"

"Okay, you've been thinking… what about?"

"About you…"

"Here we go again."

"No not like that... it's always on my mind?"

"I watch you here… on you pretty bicycle…"

"Quiet man, quiet… is just the two of us talking!"

"We don't have no secret, no whisper to me."

"Walk with me out to the gate man."

"Jus' keep your hands to yourself."

"I just need to get something."

"What? What now."

"You don't trust me?"

"Truss you… After seeing you with Merline."

"Merline! A dream you a dream."

"Me must be sleepin at Wildman Street and East Queen Street, two Tuesday evening in a row then…"

"Oh she. Me can explain that man…"

"You don't owe me no explanation."

Gently pushing her: "Meet you out the gate, one sec."
Pulling down her left lower eyelid she stares him in the
face and adds: "Just remember…a see you!"
He joins her with his bicycle next to him: "Surprise!"

      "Surprise indeed… what's this all about."

      "I want to teach you to ride."

      "Me! For what?"

With a twinkle in his eye he adds: "Instead of walking
everywhere… sometimes I could lend you my bicycle!"
Not missing the ploy she adds: "So you can get me out
of the way you mean?"

      "What way… what you talking about?"

      "Alright mister don't know what I'm talking
about… I am not interested in learning…"

      "No man… you have to learn…"

      "But why."

      "I know you like bicycles from long time!"

      "Yes. So what?"

      "You can ride mine from time to time…"

      "Alright you can teach me but that's all!"

The next private lesson, Dahlia is a cyclist: "Dahlia"

      "Yes Derrick"

      "You don't want to go for a ride?"

      "You mean yu going lend me your bicycle?"

      "You are a cyclist right?"

      "Yea!"

"Well take the bicycle and go for a ride man!"
Jasmine adds: "Jus don't make Mama see you leaving."

"Okay... thanks Derrick!"

"Now we can get down to some studies."

"Derrick, your studies different from mine."

"Putoose a promise...we soon get to the book."

"If you keep yu word, then Sunday evening me and Violet and Pansy a walk to Gaiety to see a show..."

"Three girlfriends, Gaiety, alone? Can't happen."

"Never say we going alone dear...mean Derrick."

"So who you going with? A going to tell Aunt!"

"You won't tell her if a go with you though?"

"No! Because I'll be there to watch you."

"More like watch over your interest!"

Achieving synergism, they produce a by-product, as most unprotected liaisons do; in this instance 'it' is yours truly. Her bodyguard knows I'm coming because she overhears my mother telling her Gaiety girlfriends, with whom she is planning to run away to avoid the shame. Dahlia cannot say a word to Mama or Dada for fear of repercussions. I'm a sidestep in my dad's but a full detour in my mother's matriculation and life, and a bway baby as well. My dad brags to his friends: "Me have a yout on the way yu kno!"

"That man is a general..."

"To a degree.... yea mon... one on the way..."

"Den is which one gone up?"
"Hhm her parents, have to go hide the girl!"
"You mean sequester?"
"Yea… yea, maybe a Manchester."
He needs no sequestration
to avoid the shame,
the unwanted fame,
the stigma,
the ridicule that comes
with the typical female
teenage mother lode:
a mother-to-be's role,
which,
thousands of times annually,
pop up to blight
another mother's future,
permanently.

All pray
the shame wash away
drink aerated and soap water
pray that the water break even by day
and those not yet caught
forsake all breakfast meals
except the headache pill they take
in the hopes

that the foetus won't form
some get lucky
continue to swoon

Some remain childless
on such occasions
others get blighted
boy generals delighted
girls slighted
permanently united
with an unwanted
child then children.
In this vein
they continue feeling labour pain
till life's end
... insane
"Miss I, I need to talk to you bout Jasmine."
"Why me son? Can't learn? Head tough nuh?"
"No Maam."
"Me know her you know. She won't practice?"
"No Maam."
"Then what is it mi son?"
"Me spoil her Maam."
"You do what?"
"Fall har maam."
"Mi naw ear good! Say what yu say again."

47

"Is not her fault Maam."

"No wonder…her health… she really miss…"

"What she miss maam?"

"Lord what a trouble tumble down pon me."

"Me never mean it maam."

"God help me. Dat black little wretch!"

"A sorry from the bottom of me heart Maam."

"A kill the tramp."

"A tell the truth Maam, a go against her will."

"Disgrace me like this!"

"She never want to Maam."

She is speechless momentarily but regroups with: "And you still spoil up me gal pickney?"

"Yes Maam."

"But anybody hear me dying trial?"

"Won't mek yu shame Maam, we can married."

"But boy, you don't even have dry… she don't finish her schooling, no, me can't allow it."

"But me will take good care of her Maam."

"No, no, me and Willie want more for her."

"She will do everything you want her to Maam."

"Make we finish training her, when we done…"

Fretful days go by and my mother says nothing to Mama. Mama watches, listens and waits, and waits…

"How everything Jasmine?"

"Fine Mama."

"Wen las' yu see yu health?"

"Las' month Mama."

"Yu tellin me yu sister come from Red Hills since yu come from Joycee wed'n."

"Yes Mama, two time…"

"A six week now since she married."

"A two month maam."

"…Saviour pilot me, let me to thy bosom fly."

"A sleep you a sleep this time of day, Jasmine?"

"A pray me a pray ma!"

"Rock of ages… let me hide myself in thee…"
Fearing the worst she says nothing to Dada. But on day four, she corners Jasmine in the shower. Naked.

"Lord Mama a wha!"

"A you fe tell me."

"But me no do nothing Ma."

"A going to corn you ass like corn pork."
She administers a barrage of pelts to my mother's naked skin as the entire yard listens to their exchange:

"But a what me do Mama?"

"A nuh everything good fe eat good fe talk."

"Mama. Mama. Oh God. Mama!"

"A no something a go a something a come!"

"Dada! Help! Dada!"

"Make me tell him what Derrick tell me."

"A the one time we dweet ma! God Almighty!"

"You going to need him when I done with you."

"But Mama!"

"A no ask me a ask you, a tell me a tell you."

"Help!"

"All who caan hear will feel!"

"Blouse and Skirt!"

"You a curse! The boy caan even piss straight!"

"Murder! Murder!"

"Bud fly too fast, fly past them nest "

"Caca Fart!"

"A maths yu a do! A no man yu a look."

Aunt Fern rushes to her rescue finally: "Aunt I, me don't know what it is she do but…"

Both of them breathless from the whipping now, Mama stops: "You right; cockroach don't business in a fowl fight but this is almost as much yours as mine."

"What you mean Aunt I?"

"Go call the stout gut bway Derrick!"

"Aunt she in the shower! Oh my God! Derrick!"

Tenement residency offers almost no privacy. The whole yard as well as those at home next door and across the street are now privy to my impending arrival.

* * *

The odoriferous gardener with a piqued interest sits under the window on this note.

"The man say as high as them go! Him did expect fe see heaven floor board, you know, where Massa Gad draw him rocking chair when rain a fall…!"

"No such thing my brother."

The light skin wife: "Begonia put lunch on the table."

"We coming dear…"

"Pastor! Is alright if me bless the food?"

"Yes deacon, you chat me out, so me hungry…"

"A catch you drift pastor, a will make it short."

"Time is going deacon."

"Heavenly Father please bless the food and bless the cook no matter how she may look. Amen."

"Begonia! Pass here. Mek him get a good look."

"A comin pastor…. Is wat wrong pastor?"

"A was sayin' the lunch taste good."

"Thanks Pastor, excuse me pastor…" trails the air as she departs for the kitchen with deacon's eyes locked on her bodacious trailing end. As Pastors words and the deacon's winks are getting digested, Begonia fixes a tray for Tat and gives him her own mug full of lemonade. She has a growing sensitivity towards him. She quickly dismisses the thought but thinks: a better pass by the bathroom mirror… mek sure a look good before a go tell him him tray reddy… tree day in a row, dat a fix him lunch. After doing a visual she decides: me hair don't look bad but mek a jus brush back me baby hair round me forehead... tek lickle spit and brush back me eyebrows dem. She turns to leave the bathroom then thinks... "A didn't even countenance me face wid a glance...no mus glimpse meself!" and returns to the mirror to do so: me face kind of oily... better jus' damp me washrag... use lickle soap... wipe way the hile....

Her body odour is standard fare, a weapon and an asset. Weapon-like, it attaches to anyone who gets too close, attaches itself to the new host, stakes a claim by broadcasting ownership to those supressing inhibitions. To the woman of the house this odiferous tag is an asset. Miss Mary does not mind one bit, she tolerates it as par for the course. Guests and his ever-present secretary still hold their breath as long as possible whenever Begonia, whose sense of smell, which at times seems to detect the salinity of a pot on the stove, passes by, has grown to ignore the strong nasal impact her unshaved, deodorant-denied armpits thrust onto everyone else's noses.

With a smug nod of approval, she tosses her rag over the corner of the shower curtain and waltzes out. The lady of the house appears in her path: "My, my Begonia you tidying up to leave half day!"
Giggling she responds: "No mam! Just lunch time mam!"
"Then how come you gone freshen up already?"

"Is the gardener me was going to tell that me fix little lunch for him maam."

"I see it on the tray! It look as good as pastor's."

"Me never mean for that to happen maam."

"I'm not complaining me dear! Simply notice." She breaks into a wide grin and says: "You like him?" The floor's suddenly interesting: "Can call it dat maam."

"A never take a good look... a have to now." Begonia asks: "A true maam?"

"Yes is true."

"Hhhhmmm."

"So Begonia, I know it couldn't be his hair!"

"You mean him dreadlocks maam?"

"Is that what you call it?"

"Is him tell me that maam."

"Is that what you like about him?"

"No maam... sort of maam..."

"Then what is it then girl, tell me!" She confides: "Someting 'bout him eyes maam."

"Well don't let me keep you from looking into them, you go give him his lunch...matter of fact!"

"Yes maam!"

"You can invite him into the kitchen."

"Thanks maam."

She goes outside to locate him and when she does she casually says: "Oh, is round here-so you is... you know me walk round the whole yard looking for you?"

"Looking for I?"

"Yes."

"Seek and ye shall find."

"Den yu nuh see me find you."

"I man never lost I man is right here!"

"So a see."

"So why seek I an I."

"A fix some lunch for you."

"Respek."

"What?"

"Respek! Thanks. Yu kno'"

"Oh! Yu welcome."

"Carry it forward to the I nuh."

"Wha!"

"Bring it come give I nuh!"

"Come eat in the kitchen nuh! A don't eat yet."

"So I an I need fe come inside fe eat."

"No… a wish a could come out here…but…"

Rising he approaches her; she freezes as he breaches the expected interpersonal distance: "Dat girl want I an I fe have lunch wid har."

Her neck suddenly starts itching, she reacts to it, then it's her thigh, she responds, she is awfully hot, just about every pore on her skin embarks on a body cooling assignment, sweat beads across her previously cool face, she sighs and tries to break her intertwined fingers against each other, her hairy armpits expand her blouse's sweatmark and she says: "Yea... you can come in out of the sun hot for a little... if yu want..."

"I man know that."

"Then come nuh!"

"I man don't waan do dat." Cogitating, he scratches the hairs on his right jaw with his left hand then adds: "No I man cyaan do that."

"Why." She self-consciously asks.

"When I an I sit with I Queen I man must fresh and clean. Seen!"

"What 'seen' mean?"

"Ovastan."

"What."

"I an I not to say such a word but just because..."

"Because what?"

"...Because I man check fe you still..."

"What the word 'seen' mean?"

"It mean understand to you...but ovastan to I."

"So why you don't just say that to me?"

"I man is under no man, all under is ovah! Seen!"

"Seen! I guess."

"Irie."

"So you want me bring yu lunch out here?"

"Yea, I man woulda like that, seen?"

55

"Why?"

"Too much noise een dere right now."

"Noise! Me no hear no noise, pastor talkin!"

"Is de noise dat."

"Yu believe dat."

"Yu? Ewe is humman sheep!"

"Excuuuuuse me…"

"Carry de lunch forward to I man…"

"Carry it come out here?"

"Consciousness reach dat girl?"

Intrigued: "What yu mean… consciousness reach me?"

"I man mean dat girl a follow I reasoning."

"When it quiet yu come een come eat with me?"

"Since I man queen insis' that queen can bring her lunch forward… come eat wid I and I seen?"

"Yu talk like you have somebody beside me out here wid yu?"

"Jah never leave I yet!"

She chuckles: "Since yu have company yu an him eat?"

"Is not the same…"

"As what?"

"Sharing a meal wid I an I queen to be… seen?"

"Me not no queen me dear."

"Dear! Deer in a pasture!"

"Regardless… me not no queen…"

"In I heart I feel like a king…"

"What that have to do wid what me jus say…"

"Lookin for a queen to call I own…"

"The drinks must turn water by now."

"Not even watah can quench I fire."

"Fire! Wat fire?"

"Stand and see no spoil no dance!"

"Dance!"

"I man a defen' romance!"

"Romance?"

"Yea all I an I need is a chance."

"Chance."

"Yea in a dalliance."

"But yu can lyrics!"

"I man don't even enter I man bag a tricks."

"Mek me go fe yu lunch."

"I an I can tell yu nuff more… a whole bunch!"

"Me can't stay now me have tings fe do."

"I man wish a could be right dere wit' you."

"Me soon come… yu mout too nice."

"I queen is the one that mek of sugar and spice."

"Awright… we wi eat together anoder time."

"I man queen wise?"

"Yu promise," she says with a wry smile.

He smiles back: "Yes dauta… I man promise."

Gleefully she smiles and turning on her thick-soled heels she adds: "A comin wid yu lunch." She leaves

57

him smiling, suckin wind thinking: I man gone clear.

* * *

She answers his question with a question: "So what happen if me sista Pepper see yu a chat chat me up?"

"How she goin find out, you goin tell her?"

"Look whe the house de… right de suh…"

"She de home?"

"Live and in the flesh."

"Me a look out fe her man, me jus tell her a she me come look for... yu can keep a secret right?"

"Somebody else can tell her yu stay de."

"So other people going decide what we do?"

"Them say trouble never set like rain."

"If rain start fall we go under a tree…"

"Dem say trees have eyes and snake have ears."

"Feget bout them man… a me and you a talk… plus thru yu me and my other girl a mash up!"

"Yu an which girl mash up!"

"Me an Kitty, man!"

"How Kitty come een a this? You jus a tell me say a yu and me sista Pepper mash up."

"Me an she mash up to! Yes man!"

"Yu neva say so a mek me mek it up."

"A true!"

"Yea…"

"What happen between you and she?"

"No go into it right now man... spoil the mood..."

"Mood?"

"Yea, you know, what me and you have going!"

"A never realise we have something going!"

"So what you call this?"

"A chance meeting... just talk we a talk. What happen everybody a leave yu?"

"No man, a makin space for the mature humman in my life. How come yu so mature though?"

"I read a lot of books."

"Where yu get books from?"

"One of Mama customer a market is librarian... she send used books for us... say we can still learn from them."

"A see!"

"That's how I chose a career."

"What is that?"

"A want to be a nurse."

"That's nice, then yu can take care o me?"

"Not just you one... take care of everybody."

"See that, a pick the right sweetheart!"

"What is that suppose to mean?"

"A pick somebody with ambition!"

"Yu can please let go of me hand now?"

"Why I mus do that?"

"Just find something else to do with it!"

"Why is that my girl?"

"It make me feel funny man."

"But that is what suppose to happen!"

"A true?"

"That lead to what man and sweetheart do?"

Faking it she says: "Me no know what that is."

He picks up on the fact she is sending him a message:

"Mek we spread out some clothes and find out no!"

Silence.

*   *   *

"Jasmine."

"Yes Mama."

"You mus come off of the choir... the scandal."

"Yes Mama."

"You have to go way till this thing blow over."

Thinking: How close me come to run way before me name gone abroad she responds: "Yes Mama."

Her hiding place, if made public, will make most teenage girls want to get pregnant. It takes place in Aunt Petal and Uncle Victor's home, some very nice digs. Aunt Petal is Dada's sister; her husband is a Customs Officer.

A mile north of our home, on the east side of Allman Town is Race Course. It's Friday evening and like a large portion of the city the family attends the cycle sports there. Mama desperately needs his help in deciding the course of action regarding their teenage daughter's pregnancy. The girls are gallivanting....

"Willie!"

"Wait till after the race no Iris man!"

"Awright but we must talk."

"Awright me lose anyway…what is it, talk nuh!"

"Me know after cycle sport you and Fitzy them like to go down to Missa Cox but we need to talk."

"'Bout what now Iris?"

"Shame, we have to sen way Jasmine."

"Where we going to send her? Back a country?"

"You mad! Is me yu want me mother kill?"

"If Mum kill yu what me would do."

"You would miss me Willie…"

"Yes. So where we going to send her?"

"'Round to your sister on East Road."

"Who Petal? Yu plan fe reward the gal?"

Planning to have a large family, Aunt Petal and her husband acquire a big house with two spare bedrooms. She gets her own chateau, enough for four tenement families, enjoys the irony of her punishment. Aunt Petal: "Yes Iris, me know me have to discuss it with Victor but it's all right, she can stay here…"

"Girl yu don't know how me thank yu!"

"Family rally roun family in time of need."

"Yes but…"

"No trouble yu heart… it settle… finish…."

"Chile you don't know the burden… thanks."

"Done wid it all right…"

"Awright….Garden look good!"

"Everything come from country, the roses from Miss Duncie, the crotons from Sis Ethel, the hibiscus from cousin Rena and the ginger lilies from Big Yard."

"Them would get trampled where we live…"

"Well come here and enjoy them anytime."

"A love you decorative blocks… and you hedge."

"It's called Privette."

"It Pretty."

"Thanks girl…"

"Step off the veranda… see my mango trees; ackee, breadfruit, oranges, grapefruit, lime, cherry, sweetsop and naseberries, sugarcane and yams!"

"Them come from country to?"

"Every one, so we go, so we bring back sup'm."

"The place look nice."

"Yes me dear but it is something to hang a picture on the cement walls… tough as rockstone…"

"Is solid cement eh!"

"Yes me chile."

"And a love yu flooring."

"Terrazzo tile, remember my favourite colour?"

"But of course…"

"The splashes of white is me hubby's idea…"

"Him have nice taste…"

"Separate living, dining and a breakfast area…"

"But Petal this is a mansion!"

"Let me finish girl…"

"Sorry!"

"The breakfast area is wider than the veranda."

"Fancy that! What kind o windows these?"

"Plantation shutters."

"Pretty. Feel like you right outside eh."

"You know the feeling, girl you have to see this!"

"What is it?"

"My pride and joy girl… the kitchen!"

"Show me it chile!"

"I have a four burner; double oven; oil-burning stove and my refrigerator also runs off kerosene."

"The kitchen big like two rooms down town!" Aunt P continues: "And out there is the utilities wing." Mystified Mama asks: "What."

"Room for laundry, wash and iron and such."

"Girl a mansion indeed… you drop in a fat."

"With His help," she says, pointing skyward. Houses this size won't fit on the lot where I'll be living, but if it could, it would easily serve the needs of ten to twelve families. In Trench Town it would do for at least twice as many. If most girls envision this sort of purgatory, boys will be suffering from sexual abuse. Like most wives in her position, Aunt Petal stays home and has a helper to boot. Young girls like Daisy, with education equal to the fair-skinned tourist guides, 'sexytaries' and bank tellers leave the rural areas and walk door to door in neighbourhoods such as this, knocking on gate-attached mailboxes; hoping for a miracle. Uncle Victor drives a white popular British car. Ritualistically Aunt Petal walks him to the attached carport to see him off to work then closes the dual-hinged, chain-linked gate after him. Following his departure, my mother and her aunt wile away the days in seclusion.

Chapter Four

PANSY'S CONSCIENCE PRICKS HER AS
Frankie spreads the laundry atop the carpet of dried
leaves under the canopy of chocolate trees.

Perfect cover: "Baby love."

"Yea…"

"Lie down nuh!"

Her heart races too but for a different reason. She
marches to a different drummer. Sexual promiscuity at
an early age, it is said, is prevalent among the boys.
She wonders, where they get practice? An image of
her mother ten times larger than life, glares down on

her from the cocoa leaves. Mango babbles his repertoire of sweet nothings; she hears none of it. Instead, her head reverberates with the voice of her mother: "If him touch you a kill yu… if yu make him get way with it a kill yu." She snaps back to reality: "Mango!"

"Yes Baby love."

"Me can't dweet."

"Say what baby love?" He caresses her neck.

"Me can't… Mama…Mama say she wi kill me."

"Mama don't have to know, a between we!"

"Me tell yu leaf have eyes and snake have ears!"

"Yu see any snake?"

"No but me see plenty eyes in the leaf them!"

"Cho man, we reach too far to turn back."

"We? Me no gone nowhere."

"Yu hard wid me, treat me like a Chinee man."

"Me easier wid yu than everybody else."

"Yu drive a hard bargain. When yu done wash?"

"Mango man no today. Mama sick, me mind..."

He sits up abruptly: "What wrong with Miss Pinnie!"

"Me leave her in bed."

"Oh! That's why a yu one a go a river?"

Smiling she says: "You see the light!"

He sighs deeply: "Me feel bad, a pressure yu..."

"No worry bout it man. Promise me one thing."

"Wha' that?"

"When yu ready! Mek me know."

"You can wait?"

"Yes man!"

"Me have to finish big school."

"Four year!"

"And then me want to do nursing."

"But gal yu have ambition!"

"And me want to married first."

"Puss in a bag, Gad, me ded by that time!"

"I will make yu the happiest man in the worl'..."

"How come..."

"If yu wait fo me... that's for me to kno..."

"Them say wait kill man."

"Well if yu ded a wi see yu in heaven."

"How come Pepper no have your ambition?"

"Pepper is not me... I have a goal..."

"A see dat!"

"A ress me case."

"Lawd take the case and gi'e me the pillow..."

"Frankie!"

"Yes baby."

"Yu making the right decision."

"I know that baby love."

"Yea! But yu don't know exactly what me mean!" "Well since me not a mind reader..."

"You want to guess?"

"Dauta yu have me so confuse… what."

"You want me tell you?"

"Yes do that nuh!"

"Yu find a woman, boy."

Frankie returns to the district with a look of ambiguity, a friend asks: "Boy Mango if me Horse Mouth never know better me'd say you madda ded, how you look so man!"

"How you mean?"

"Part o' yu look like you mumma dead and part look like you find a Panya Jar full of old pirate money."

"Boy in a way you right."

"Yu mean pon the two count? What yu mean?"

"Me no conquer de ting, but me love har still."

"Love! Wid who?"

"The said little ting that me never conquer!"

"But Mango you not making any sense!"

"It plain as day star!"

"Wha… wha yu a talk bout?"

"The reasoning that Pansy show me is some reasonin' nobody else ever show me yet!"

"Yu mean little Pansy!"

"Little Pansy turn big Pansy!"

"So what happen to Pepper?"

"Pepper! Pepper get a beaten."

"Fe truth!"

"Boss the girl ask me fe wait... and yu know what? Me heart a tell me fe wait fe her."

"What yu have fe breakfast this morning star?"

"Man move an go way!"

*   *   *

For months my mother endures the sequestration-induced change in lifestyle then, in a definite physiological contradiction to the relaxed atmosphere, she becomes hypertensive and the escalating blood pressure interferes with her health. She experiences episodes of eclampsia and is rushed to the Kingston Jubilee Hospital. Induction of premature labour stops the 'fits' and saves our lives. I, Youtman arrive prematurely into this struggle we call life, in the Labour Ward, on February 14th, 1953, seven months after the 'Add Maths' class. Four and a half pounds of Yardie, screaming in response to the Euro-centric welcome, the slap of Dr. Strangelove's palm on my black backside. My premature birth warrants a fortnight's hospital observation detention so my mother and I bond in the time medically specified for her recuperation. Through the portals of my incubator, she showers me with love and affection and has a difficult time leaving me in the care of the medical staff. She goes home alone to face the scandal and speculation as to the need for her vacation.

African customs call for a fortnight's isolation of a newborn and its mother, to get acclimated to the world's germs. Home now for eight weeks, I'm afflicted with a terrible cold, breathing is almost impossible; Mama offers words of prayer to The Africanised version of the English introduced God she serves: "Father God, a thank you for my grandson. Thank you for blessing us with this child. Please God, if you can just make him a healthy child. Father God you and you alone are the miracle worker. A pray for these and all other mercies in Thy name. Amen." My godmother, Mama's friend from up the lane, Miss Icilda, saves me from its life-threatening clutch by waiting for me to try to exhale; then she inhales all the phlegm from my lungs and upper alimentary canal into her mouth then 'tweh,' deposits it on the dirt outside. Rid of my cold, I am propped up in a bath pan with old clothes as bolsters so I can check out my new environment and be inspected by my all island family. I am boxed into our room and placed on the floor to learn to creep. Church sisters, too indirect to ask a straightforward question come by: "We not really poking our nose sister dear, but we just come by to see what happen to Jasmine!" Mama: "That's funny! In church Sunday a say howdy and nobody speak! How come you never ask me then!"

"You know bout after church sister dear."

"Yes, a know…"

I remain quiet as a church mouse.

Our new living accommodations force me to acquire my walking skills in the barren yard, competing with chicken, ducks, scurrying rats and their faeces for real estate. I encounter society's next barrier, the yard fence. No open country here, everything is done to keep one circumspect. I learn to talk. When we go walking up the lane, I return with the same words on my lips: "Mama, a see Lilly! And she got a leg!"

"Iris Oh."

"Yes Willie."

"Gad naw sleep yu kno."

"Praise The Lord, yu accept Him Willie?"

"Mek yu hasty so missis… hear me nuh!"

"Sorry Willie."

"Gad keep me grandson little, give me a jockey!"

"So the 'damn, come from yonder, stout gut boy', as yu like to call Derrick do yu a favour!"

"It look so sweetheart."

He and his typical male friends, descendants from the 'Dark Continent', in their crisis-filled lives, play 'Pick-a-pow' and bet on the horses. Through me, he hopes to vicariously enjoy his true love; to be a jockey; one day, through his protégé he'll retire early; that as his

71

jockey, I will acquire all his lusted-for trappings right here on The Rock; in the here and now, ease his misery, provide financial security as the answer to his problems.

But a private war brews between my grandparents. Like most men, he's of the philosophy that Church is a spiritual club for women and children. The few men running the gauntlet in early to mid life develop solid spiritual mettle, the consistency of which is tested time and time again by his alcoholic, gambling, philandering peers. The partying male, when he surprisingly reaches old age, marches to a different drum. Beginning in his late sixties, he becomes a church visitor. In his seventies, he sings to a different tune; he becomes a regular visitor to his wife's church and takes only an occasional drink. At eighty, he definitely finds Gad. Soon, it becomes impossible for him to attend church unaided. Homebound, he worships by proxy.

My father finishes school and in practising his version of: 'Variety is the spice of life' is scoping out a young miss from Old Harbour Bay. He works at The Sanatorium simultaneously keeping tabs on the upper crust's medicated eccentrics and some poor, mad inmates. In general, employees with ambition and savvy at office politics can make it up the curry-favour ladder to become a civil servant --a servant none the less. A little less melanin doesn't hurt. He steps up from the bicycle, affords himself a used car so he can stretch his legs even further afield. He has another man-child, which gestates for the full term and arrives a full ten months after my birth, on December 14th. A third, of similar-aged 'oats', which he keeps under raps, comes to light later. He proposes and the Old Harbour Bay girl's parents are not as definitive about their daughter's long-range plans as Mama is, so sometime during the following year, he becomes a married man doing the right thing for one out of three boys.

* * *

The in house conversation fades from his consciousness, replaced by visions of…. Begonia returns; he is still squatting, suckin wind and wearing a wide grin that exposes all thirty-two of his miraculously retained, pearl whites. She returns the facial expression but shows what he considers an attractive space in her upper jaw where a pre-molar resided.

"So what dat dauta bring fe de I eat?"

"Look nuh! See it here!"

"Righteous… no pork no een de?"

"A know better than that."

"No. Ansa I… dat een deh?"

"No man nuh dat nuh een deh."

"Respek."

"Yu sure yu no want to come een?"

"Naw man. I man cool; seen?"

"If yu say so…"

"Yea man, dat girl can gwaan go eat. Respek."

"Awright, if yu need more drinks call me hear?"

"Dat girl waan drown I man?"

"No… if yu want anything else den… feel free."

"I man free… yu kno… always…"

Taking a mouthful he looks her up and down approvingly, nods, smiles and says: "But I man wi member dat still." She hides her approving smile with the sashaying back of her skirt then heads inside.

Still enjoying the last bites of his meal dreddie dreams dreams of Begonia and himself and she returns with gleeful eyes: "How was yu lunch?"

"I man could get use to this yu kno."

"Yu telling me that yu like it?"

"Dat girl brilliant?"

"A never say suh?"

"I know. I man say dat."

"Mek me tek the tray…"

"Tanks… I man can walk dat girl home?"

"This evening? Yes man, yes man!"

"I man don't want no jealous one attack I still."

"Yu don't have to worry bout that."

"Me and me old boyfrien bruk up last week."

"How dat happ'n?"

Raising her eyebrows she looks him dead in his pupils:
"Him tired of hearing me talk bout a certain dread!"
He smiles, a look of bemusement in his eyes and asks:
"Which dread dat?"
She puts her right hand akimbo, rocks back on the hip
then deadpans: "I give yu one deggae deggae guess."

* * *

Jacks Hill Daisy: "Hi Clover! What happen stranger!"
Rosie: "Yea, yu move follow yu married an fegat we."
Leonard: "Lawd tek it easy, gi'e har a chance fe
explain."
Jacks Hill Daisy glances around sheepishly and in a
lower voice adds: "Tailor wife must have found out
about you?"
Claude: "Yes, somebody tell her. In Morant Bay."
Fitzy: "Clover, more than two year me no see yu."
Clover: "I should ha' follow me mind... don't come..."
Fitzy: "How you treat we! Me never think yu would!"
Jacks Hill Daisy: "A don't condone it, but is not she
alone cause what transpire to transpire!"
Rosie: "A serious thing!"
Jacks Hill Daisy: "You men! Exhibit some control nuh!"
Claude: "All the same though Fitzy is true my girl
talkin... down a Missa Cox the other eveling, we did
get on the subject... yu shudda did hear him!"
    "Yea! What him say?"

"Say him lawyer friends object to de behaviour!"

Leonard: "Royal blen!"

"Yea… say it is a crime agains' humman."

Jacks Hill Daisy: "I really can't understand why some of you men run 'bout so! Look at Claude and I!"

Leonard: "Well yu are a special case… yu an him!"

She turns admiringly to look at Claude as she asks him: "And whatever do you mean by that!"

Claude puts a finger over his lips: "Mek it ress..."

Jacks Hill Daisy flashes her boyfriend a knowing smile and he yields the floor because yielding to her, is to allow the one who is educating him, to do the same to the others: "Their penchant is criminal!"

Fitzy: "What the hell you just say?"

Rosie: "Yea, finish what you saying girl chile."

Clover: "Yu speakin' more like yu uptown boss lady."

"Actually I am no longer there you know!"

"Really! Where yu is now?"

"I am actually in training to be a teacher!"

"But girl yu get out! Congratulation… good to see some of we get out… mek something of we self…"

Claude: "Clover yu don't realise it but yu just start something right now."

"Really! Wha dat?"

"Man pick up nickname by them actions…"

"A know… but wat dat have to do wid me?"

"Hol on mon... patience... patience..."

"Awright... yu see what yu jus said when yu heard that Daisy trainin to be a teacher?"

She has to think for a minute: "Yu mean 'Get-Out'?"

"Yeah."

"What about it?"

"Jus give her a name. Clover meet 'Get-Out'!"

"I can't believe you'd do such a thing to me?"

"Really! Watch me... GET-OUT!"

"Oh my God! I don't believe this."

Leonard jumps to her defence: "Girl child leave it alone... you will only make it worse..."

Clover tries: "Can we get back to what we discussin?"

Jacks Hill Daisy: "Aw well... I was saying, is lack of education that causes the behaviour."

Fitzy: "What yu mean by that?"

Jacks Hill Daisy: "Most of you still operate under your ancestral ways with multiple partners' practices."

Fitzy still confused: "What yu say to that Daisy?"

"We live here now."

Fitzy: "What that mean?"

"Plain and simple! In a new land with new laws! You change you ways to the order in this society!"

* * *

'Born under the clock' has special significance in the rural areas. To a Kingstonian in the 'country' it bestows conversational clout. Rural illiterates assume that because a Kingston illiterate speaks with a citified accent, then he must know what he is talking about. So skilful members of this accent club extrapolate their vernacular into muscle, respect, physical presence and a positive aura. I miss the clout boat because we move to 'country' when I attain the ripe old age of two years, too young to assimilate the lingo. When my grandfather sits to work, I sit on the presser foot, between his feet and sway from side to side as he pedals.

* * *

When Ivy joins her father in the field, her face does not hide the fact that something is awry.

"Papa! Mama send me come help yu sar."

"A what wrong with her?"

"Me never say nothing do her sar." She says.

"Pickney yu no have to say nothing, she been coming a bush with me before you born."

Averting his gaze she tries to make light of the situation and deflect any stress he may be feeling: "A true Papa, a so long you and she a come a bush?"

He rests his crossed arms atop his pitchfork, a smile on his face, he reminisces: "Gal a tell yu… make it stay anyway."

"A wha' Papa?"

"Nutten."

"Cho Papa man, tell me man!"

"A how old you be now."

"Me a sixteen sah."

"Hhhmm."

"A wha Papa?"

"Make me siddung little."

"Tell me a wha no sah," she tugs at his arm.

"The first day me and you mother spend, she did follow me come a bush..."

"A true Papa!"

"A from that time me a work this piece of land."

"A so it go sah!"

"Yes me pickney and except when she stay home to have you and you sister, she never miss a day."

"Me never know! So you an Mama do it Papa!"

"Any time we could spend together, we did it..."

"Papa you sound romantic bad!"

"You think me and yu mother dead?"

"Alright Papa!"

"Me wi really miss har if anything happen..."

"Me know Papa."

"How yu know?"

"A no one and two time yu boot touch me foot when yu a play with fe her own under the table Papa?" He rises, dusts off his bottom: "...Pansy with her?"

"No Papa, she gone wash."

"Little Pansy?"

"Me a teach her long time Papa."

"Then a everybody clothes she a wash?"

"No Papa, we do de delicate dem at home."

"A so no, me no know…"

He turns to look at her. Right into her eyes: "So tell me wha wrong with yu mother?"

Disarmed she has to come clean: "Papa a nothing much… just gas… she drink little ginger tea and a lie down little…" she turns to look at the path by which she came then adds: "As a mater of fact she might soon come now…"

"Right, mek we look 'bout some market goods."

"Now you come Papa."

Chapter Five

IN OUR SYMBIOTIC LIVING, WE SHARE WATER
with the mosquitoes and their larvae. To avoid ingesting
them, we slap the surface of the water, serving notice
to the tenants: fly off or dive for cover. In rain-deficient
times we ferry kerosene tins, balanced hands-free, on
our cottered heads, from the river for domestic needs
and from the spring for drinking. During drought
conditions we ingest the bacteria-laden river water that,
requires time, aeration and filtration through the sand
and long runoff periods for purification. The river is a

high-usage, multi-tasking artery and to attain any semblance of purification its water must be collected either very late at night or early in the morning.

The disparity in building products distinguishes the subcultures. Very few folks live in lavish homes. Some have tiny huts with thatch roofs and name-tarnishing furniture. We practice one-up-man-ship: "Joy! My house better than yours, we have zinc roof." Joy, fed up being put down: "A thatch but a fe we."

"My bed a coir mattress yours a banana trash. Rat and mongoose belly further from ground than it."

It takes a strong constitution to tolerate the stench of the planned obsolescence, gypsy-like outhouses. The genteel crowd craftily visit the privy under the cloak of darkness. The repositories' contents are metaphors to disliked individuals: "Yu smell like behind pit toilet!"

At critical mass the mess will spread. Moving the outhouse to a new pit creates a spot of liquid gold as all things planted in its wake produce crops with abundant yield.

Men, in their multi-partnering behaviour coupled with condescending women create an atmosphere wherein it is impossible to always have two-parent households. Menial existences and job opportunities may force mothers to leave the children with friends or relatives, migrate, then send for them. The English,

The cacophony seeps into my consciousness like a mudslide into an expectant valley. In folklore the cock's crowing indicates that it's five a.m. I am excitedly aware, for the first time, at this hour, due to the day's significance, I am six years old today.

The second vocal stab pierces a hole in the damp night-air like a ground-bound star apple on its pre-rupture rush to kiss the dirt. It's Judas the Red Hampshire's reply. His perch, due north behind my home, is a foothill of The Bull Head Mountains. Their pecking order dynamics mixes with other night sounds: the mate-seeking calls of croaking lizards, screech owls, frogs, crickets and self-illuminating capays.

Casper now signals his authority. This leghorn's natural plumage causes him to strut with his in near-fighting cock stance. It's poetic justice that he who struts and crows too much cuts himself short in terms of ruts. Most offspring in his henhouse share the neighbourly Red Hampshire's looks.

'Bungscious, with his black plumage and bright red comb, completes the pecking order dynamics of their quadraphonic 'bang-ga-rang'. When fighting, he skilfully flies vertically, a foot in the air, to inflict damage with his spurs. His ancestors must have cut their teeth, so to speak, in cockfighting arenas. With his bodacious crowing, the others cease responding.

Atop the bureau separating both beds in my room is Mama's handmade, white, stiffly starched scalloped crochet piece. Nestled in it, is an angular patterned lead crystal vase with an assortment of plastic roses. The spring-wound-lime-green clocks' luminous markings state it's a quarter past three. The flame of the soot-filled, translucent kerosene lamp's shade with its insignia "Home Sweet Home" mutely reassures me that all's well. Everything's copasetic, cook and curry.

Profiling adjacent to it is a clear plastic elliptical dome, with sky-blue background "Five and Dime" replica of New York City's skyline as Atlantis, Lady Liberty's one hundred fifty two feet and 'Boy'hattan's submerged skyline sports a proportionately represented twenty feet of plastic snow and a hundred and seventy one feet of water.

This time of night sleep normally sweet bad. But today is special. As excited as I am I must wait on the sun to sling radiant spears onto the misty hillsides at higher elevations before I rise. Anxious for daybreak, I rub my eyes seemingly in an attempt to diffuse the darkness. Pensive: I picture all the activities daylight will bring. The games my friends and I will play; but all of this is delayed until long after morning bus passes.

* * *

"I queen!"

"Yes I dread"

"Is a while since I man a walk I queen home."

"This eveling make two month and four day."

"I man queen is a almanac?"

"No I. I jus keep track of special tings."

"Well I man have a ting fe share wid I queen."

"Oh, one month was short... share it nuh..."

"I man pick up a vibes pon the slave seen!"

"What kind a vibes dat?"

"Preacher get some land from a faward one..."

"Yea... from Sister Nora that dead?"

"Yea... said dauta... an she no ded."

"Wha she do?"

"She faward I."

"Yea! I mus memba dat."

"So wha happen now wid de lan?"

"Her pickney dem all gone a Hinglan... her Bredda and two sista faward a'ready... a so-so cousin she have leff back... dem neva even pay her bad mind, so she will the property to the church. Why you so interested inna it though?"

"Well I man want build a gates pon it."

"So say whey dey pon yu mind nuh."

"Say what?"

"The real reason why you interested into land and house building man!"

"Real reason! Wha yu a talk bout?"

"Dat dat man want fe de wid I!"

"A no news dat!"

"But I want hear it."

"Jus feel the vibes an seckle queen. Seen?"

"Man miss I a nite time don't?"

He looks around to ensure they are alone. He can ill-afford to have his next statement fall on the wrong ears. Convinced they are alone he replies: "Well, I man queen could say that. I man miss her."

"See that wasn't so hard?"

"Jus no tell no one say I man say dat."

"It safe nyah, bout de lan… I wi ask Miss Mary."

"I man can deal wid the preacher man man!"

"She no deal, she wuk pon pastor…do it I way nyah."

"What a gwaan that I man don't know bout?"

"I tell Miss Mary, from she done know, we wi get it."

"She done know what? She want the lan?"

"Bout what a gwaan…evenin time she come tell me my boyfriend waitin fo me! So if it is allright…?"

"A oh! Awright….yea man! Do that nuh!"

"Respek."

"No! Respek!"

* * *

Across the river, near the spring, Canepiece Rat, my friend, exists under more austere accommodations. Kitchen Bitch empty, his room's illumination is left to the man in the moon. If he's awake, his eyes must make do with the moonlight bridging the gaps between the planks and Z' shaped frame of his wooden window which has no curtain. Crude leather straps hinge the window to the frame.

Diagonally to the east, across the main road from me, Ackee Red is missing all of this. His mother must wake him every morning to prevent him from sleeping until nightfall. Between their homes, the river is kept at bay by the gigantic chicken wire enclosures, packed with riverbed excavated rocks, we call 'grines': Attributed to their grinding against each other before finding a permanent resting position. They are used to resist catastrophic soil erosion in the river's inundated waters.

As the day starts to peep, I run into the adjoining room and jump into Mama and Dada's bed and under the-body-heat-generated warm covers startling them both into consciousness: "Mama! Dada! Yu a sleep? Remember say a me birthday today!" Boxed in, Mama, sans her dentures, which are grinning at Dada from a glass on the bureau, pulls me closer: "Sonny, yu don't need to member me. Me even member the day yu born like it was yessiday."

"A true Mama?"

"Yes son me taking yu to Spaalin wit me today!"

"A lie yu a tell! Sorry Mama. A true Dada?"

"Yes sonny, go visit yu godmodher."

Me nearly jump out of the bed, "Say wha'! Dada! Mama a carry me pon bus! Yu a carry me go look for Goddie Una!" I say this shaking him but shaking me. Dada rubbing my scalp like a bowler does a cricket ball before release, says, "Yes Sonny boy, a true. We make dat plan. You glad?"

"Dada! Me glad so till me glad bag wan' bu's'."

"Alright Sonny, wash yu face and brush yu teet."

He gets up in standard fare --flour bag boxer shorts and merino-- and pours some water from the goblet into the face-basin on the cistern. On my tiptoes I reach my toothbrush, dab it in the water, and then sparingly apply, then use the baking soda as toothpaste. After rinsing, I pass my wet palm back and forth atop the soap then smear a thin lather on my face and quickly wash it off. I use the stiffly starched green hand towel with an embroidered, yellow in-flight butterfly to do a one-swipe dry. I exchange the doorknob garb, out of my pyjamas into my judging clothes I race down the non-landing interrupted flight of stairs with bragging on my mind and relatively cold air creeping up the legs of my short-pants onto my behind.

I snatch my milk bottle off the ledge, dash towards the four-by-four-by-three-deadbolt secured exit: "Rev!" An irritated reply: "Wha you want."

"The back door open?"

"Yu don't see me getting ready to feed the pigs?"

"So wha that say?"

"Yu a fool. You think me can feed them in the pig pen from in the house!"

I interpret his comment and dash round the corner, into the street and tackle the two serpentine miles of hilly roads with requisite boyhood paraphernalia: catapult in my right side pocket and a few pebbles in the other and barefooted. With no help from fertility sensing dogs and a narrow window per year in which cows are fertile, Dada's network of friends use a sixth sense to determine when the cows are in oestrus. Their excellent animal husbandry leaves only rare periods during which Mama has to resort to coconut or her biased preference, sweetened condensed milk, to add colour to his coffee or our chocolate tea.

Other young boys and I go at cross-purposes to fetch the milk. Me, I'm going up the road today, west. An acquaintance approaches from the far side of town.

"Mawnin Man Rat," I say.

"Mawnin Youtman," he stops and tilts his head with a quizzical look: "Me and you always pass one another why we no just get the closest milk and satisfy?"

"Ask you parents if you brazen enough…"

"Me? No Maasa… me jus a joke!"

"Me know… yu wouldn' backchat dem!"

"How you look so happy this mornin?"

"Me birthday, me granny a carry me pon bus!"

"You lie! Yu lie! Go where!"

"Spaalin."

"Carry back something for me yu hear?"

With my palm outstretched: "Gimme the money no!"

"You too mean, me gone!"

Soon after passing the Higglers and their gathered produce awaiting the bus I forgo the river-paralleling road's serpentine layout for the first of my many obstacle-filled shortcuts. Landowners and nature conspire to protect the properties in a variety of ways: Our 'national deadbolt', Barbed wire; Reduced visibility because of shadows; The dripping orange leaves; And condensation challenged watergrass; spider webs.

I avoid most of the spider-webs as I am too agile for the ambitious sentinels, but I take a bath in the tall watergrass and must constantly be on the lookout for the yellow blossoms at the end of the arcing

Spanish Needles that create a pattern with the green undergrowth. Going through Massa Knightengale, the local land baron's orange grove, I must be on the lookout for Watchie. I'd hate to be mistaken for a little orange tief and have this man, a relative, make me into a duppy. The first of the west bound busses with its high centre of gravity producing carrier, laden with crocus bags stuffed; with all manner of market-bound farm produce passes me twice. The din of its engine fades and intensifies on its serpentine mountain climb.

Maas Aaron, a hard-working farmer and herdsman in his day, has suffered the double tragedy of losing his common law wife to cancer and the amputation of both his legs below the knees. Diabetes. Still, he farms, sitting, and cares for the only children he has around, his goats. From the sheen possessing, swept dirt-floor of his, villagers-built, one-room-thatch-hut, he views the passing world through the doorless doorway. As a matter of commonly practised courtesy we must speak. He has difficulty hearing so I must compensate. In satisfying his obvious anticipation, I speak loudly: "Mawnin Mass Aaron."

He has news for me: "Me goat got kid."

I muse: Poor soul no got nobody: "A howdedo me a tell you sah."

Oblivious to my respect and obviously full of excitement he responds: "A two kid him got." I am well adjusted to our custom of being mannerly, so I perpetuate the tradition: "A mawnin' me a tell you sah." Eyeing the vista-changing, approaching wall of citrus, I quicken my pace and think: Tenk Gaad the citrus wi soon block him. "A ram and she."

*   *   *

"Mawning Maas Joe-Joe."

"Mawnin Youtman."

"Me come early again this morning sar."

"Yes boy. Aunt wi get the best part of the milk."

Beatrice is set up for milking next to his cement block and steel (CBS), ambitiously started three bedrooms, drawing room, dining hall and veranda dream home. Only one bedroom of his CBS home is complete. Been completed with zinc roof and three-foot square Celotex ceiling for over a year now. The other rooms are a hump of dirt surrounded by erect brick walls that have heaven for a ceiling. Planks of wood make pathways through the hollow rooms. The cow and calf overnight near the pipe-dream living room because a minority population, having a disinterest in animal husbandry, but an interest in the cash cow concept creates a small band of strange bedfellows who will take your cow to market and obliterate your plans to wean and sell a healthy calf, milk her dry and put her out again. I extend a greeting to his wife who is in the kitchen tending to the ground-based, three stones, pot-supporting fireside: "Good mawning Miss Dan."

Squatting next to the fireside, the surplus fabric of her ancient dress tucked tightly between her knees, she speaks to me through the green wattles of razor sharp bamboo that makes the sides of her new kitchen: "Mawning Youtman, you look extra bright this morning."

Staring at her beading forehead as she scrapes yesterday's ashes and throws them at the root of a nearby coffee tree as fertilizer, I reply: "Thank you Maam. A because Mama a carry me pon bus today Maam."

Backing away from the slow motion, mushrooming spread of the airborne ashes she continues: "But yu is a lucky little boy." Facing me now and still smiling with her apparently ever-weary eyes framed by whisker-like-crows-feet-bracketed eyelashes, a toothless grin, but for one upper and a corresponding lower incisor, she grabs her skirt-tail and returns to the kitchen and starts scouring, with some remaining ashes, the small burnt pot she uses to make his coffee: "But how yu so lucky me son?"

"Is me birthday Maam."

"Oh a see. Then yu is how much?"

"Me tun six tidday Maam."

As the saying goes, "Cow never know de use a dem tail 'til fly start tek it" and like stamp to a letter, tenacious remnants of last night's post cud-chewing, second digestion, are attracting just about all the houseflies that are on call in the region. They are as persistent as the calf now on a short leash to keep it a bay while Maas Joe-Joe ambidextrously pulls and pushes on the teats while using the top of his fist to duplicate the calf's snout by rythmically applying pressure to her udders. His expert ear keys on the resonance of the initial squirts as they ricochet off the bottom of the bucket and from the thousand droplets he's able to gauge the day's productivity. He angles my quart bottle and using direct injection fills it without spilling a drop: "Me goin gi yu the best part of the milk. Yu can take it as yu birthday present."

"Thank yu sah."

"No thank me yet... afta the bubbles settle..."

"How come yu only get little bit of bubbles sah?"

After being pensive he says: "Because a mek the milk run down the side of the bottle to the bottom."

"Oh sah!"

"Tailor and Aunt and dem odder one awright when yu leff dem?"

"Yes sah."

Miss Dan, overhearing everything from the kitchen chimes in: "Tenk Gad fe Jeezas."

The aroma of her activity wafts in our direction: the aroma of smoke and fry soda dumplings --a mixture of flour, cornmeal, a touch of salt and baking soda kneaded into a tight batter.

"Me a walk go ova desso sah…" I excuse myself and follow my nose, back to the doorway of the source. Miss Dan seeing my thinly-veiled lust beckons: "Come for yu birthday present me son. It hot."

I hastily outstretch my hand, smile then take it in my palm: "Thanks Maam." Thinking to myself: Gad Almighty it hot bad! I promptly push it into my pocket then hastily pull the fabric away from my leg as the heat telegraphs intentions of first and second degree burn injuries to my brain. Good Gad: I think, this dumpling feel like it still on the fire. Still uncomfortable, I rip two, relatively cold, dew-laden coffee leaves from a nearby tree to make an insulator for my left hand and transfer it there for a while.

"Come Youtman. Come cork you milk."

I walk away: "Thanks Miss Dan, me gone maam."

"Walk good me boy."

"Thank yu sah."

I don't intend to have a burn scar in my hand either; I prefer it in my mouth, so I begin working on my dumpling. My hamlet is lost in the dense vegetation. The landscape seemingly chases the heavens through the early morning smoky-blue-hue of good wood. Under scorched butter pans or cheap, leaky-rivet-holed dented pots with orange or lime-leaf-brewing tea or pre-strained coffee and black Duchies and three-legged pots with quattie hot fat ejecting the remnants of the shopkeepers' watered-down oil. The valley on my right bottoms out and nestles the river in Low-Woods, Mango's domain. Hills rise to Jericho, Cumberland and Banana Ground where Miss Pinnie's farmland is located. It is here that Ivy comes to collect crops her father gathers for the market; it is where she meets Superman on many occasions then clandestinely goes to the river to bathe. When word of their affair started spreading, Gang Gang Galina puts it into words: "Him a carry straw fe her."

Me Johnnycake done.

I want to stop and rest my hands but the johnnycake has me thinking breakfast. And the bus ride. I regain a brisk downhill pace. The trees, spider webs and water grass are still pregnant with dew. I take my baths.

Chapter Six

IN THE BURG MY NEIGHBOURS COME ALIVE. Ackee Red's older brother Mongoose is teasing Miss Birdie's son Bull. Bull should not be teased really, he is delusional, a condition, it is rumoured, he suffers since he father left for England. And took six years before he had a single letter written to his mother. He mostly emanates the moo sound of a cow. "You mus' t'ink yu a bull cow, yu always have grass in yu mout', can't say nutten but mooo."

"A who yu a call cow! Yu see me with no horn?"

"Numbady no call yu cow, yu a man! Bull!"

"Bull! Bull! Who yu a call bull!"
Wrong move. It sticks.

Buddy her second son is so robust, fat has separated his brain. He has two personalities, one, few hands short of a bunch! He has two names Boy-us and Buddy. We poke fun at him every chance we get. Push the right buttons and he will show he has a screw loose: "Good morning buddy!" Launches him into a private two-person conversation: speaks quickly as if he's being pressured to finish his diatribe in a prescribed time, his retort:

"Morning Buddy? Me no buddy fe you?
Then a who? A Ma Ma buyer
With a buyer of a goat. With a goat goat cord
With a cord call follow. Wid a follow follow ma.
With a Ma Maa do do. Is a kid called Flash
With flash flash call. Call to her mother say baaay
From the cord of a leash. To the leash is a man
And the man name Bennett! Missa Bennett?
Missa Bennett play de fiddle fo' the young gal
Then a who the gal. A gal called Rosie.
Rosie den dat a fe me gal!
Missa Bennett say woe cow!
Ask him where it is that he's off to?

YOUTMAN Saturday's Child

Standard reply, "Boy, us a go up so or us a go down so you kno'... go see what a gwaan!" Then looking to his side "No true?" He nods to his imaginary friend and they leave.

Fifty yards from home, Pansy, Frankie's moth-flower is tardy in sending her smoke signals to the fire gods. Saturday affords her the luxury of going at her own pace. Miss Pinnie left on the bus to sell her wares in the market. On any other morning her disciplinarian mother can be heard berating her: You better get up out of the bed and go ketch the fire, put down the book me carry come give yu till we eat done..."

To my left the green wood in Miss Kelly's dirt-floor fireplace, thatch kitchen chokes among the Robusta bananas behind Cou'n Mary's shop. Thin wisps of smoke escape through the thatch of dry coconut palm fronds. Thermal packages make their way to the triangular portholes at the apex of its opposite ends. Cou'n Mary's fireside is the last to get lit on account of the amount of late night company she keeps. She married young to Breadfruit Crop, an ancient Busha for a fossilized Buckra and mentioned to him, her wish: "Busha Baby oh!"

"Yes me baby!"

"Yu know what a wish for daalin!"

"No me pet... what yu wish for?"

"Yu baby want a shop."

"But sweetie we no have the land for shop!"

"Little jam to corner putoose, exercise books, Bulla cake, crackers, bun and cheese and sweetie."

"Yu waan cater mostly to school pickney?"

"That's all me need Busha Baby… jus wan lickle sup'm to keep me busy when yu gawn a bush." He grants her her wish, a single room, tiny shop, at the entrance to the 'S' bend, at our town's eastern end. Business suffers during the holidays: "Boy Busha Baby… school on holiday, might as well lock up…"

"Lock up nuh love… it no putting pot a fire…"

"It keep me occupy… if me sell little liquor…" Word of an attractive bartender on a secluded corner and away from the maddening crowd and pairs of eyes that peers and gossips with people that know their missis' spreads and like ants following fat motorists of male description risk damage to their vehicles, park them precariously, even though, in the heart of town, there are two more convenient emporiums. With time, taxi drivers' stay ever longer and ever later. The signals they send convince her she is better off leaving him. She does, rents a shop in town and is doing well; brags to everyone that listens: "Is me shop business cause me to send Cherry go a boarding school. And when she finish me a send her go a England go study nursing!"

Two obligatory bottles of rum, a dozen aerated waters, a student and housewife's bare essentials. Rewarding.

Miss Kizzy, Parson Edwin's wife, catches the fire and sings her songs of praise thanking The Heavenly Father. She asks that He not only guides but also carries her on her way. She's loud in her prayers, selfish too, just me. Me, me oh God...

Smoke curls skyward next to the spring across the river. In Cistern Rat's kitchen amid some chocolate trees, his granny Nana Lou is suffering from smoke inhalation and the green bananas for breakfast remains in a parboiled state. The water-soaked firewood is producing nothing but smoke and ashes. Cistern Rat got his name because during his first week at school, the cistern and dripping standpipe never ceased to amaze him. He remained there at recess, amazed at the constant drips because of a washer beyond its better days. His older brother Barby Thunder --his love for the soft yam bearing the shortened form of the island for which it's named, Barbados-- is singing loudly this morning. Predictably, the hungrier, the louder.

A little more oil in my lamp keeps it burning
A little more oil in my lamp I pray
A little more oil in my lamp keep it burning
Keep it burning till the break of day

Ackee Red and Canepiece Rat are playing by the side

Terrence R. E. Burey

of the road. I'm ecstatic: "Ackee Red, Ackee Red, Canepiece Rat, Canepiece Rat, guess wha, guess wha, guess whey Mamma a caah me go for me birt'day, guess whe', guess whey!" I add: "Him a caah me gaa Spaalin pan de bus'."

Pandemonium breaks out: "Kiss me mumma, yu lucky bad." Ackee Red shouts, running towards me.

Canepiece Rat, "Maasa yu lucky bad." And in keeping with our repetitiousness, "Yu lucky bad maa-sah. Yu a get fe go pon bus befo'e me!" He says, adding, "All the same though a no' me one nevah --never-- go 'pon bus! Ackee Red neva go pon bus yet neither, epsep --except-- when him hop it." Pregnant pause: "Yu mussy glad bad?"

"A how you know so Maasa?" I inquire.

"A yu teet' them me see."

Ackee Red adds, "How yu a 'kin them like Kahn dog."

I am not about to take such an insult without showing my resentment: "Anything you call me, a yu a it 'cause it tek one to know one." Then I hesitantly leave to deliver my cargo and rid my arms of the source of their ache. Mama, in her preferential treatment seizes my arm, "Come Sonny, follow me." As she leads the way into the enclave off the downstairs dining room; it's our morning ritual; she gives me the special brew

104

of a beaten raw egg and orange juice emulsion which she and Dada have decided will give me added brain power. I dutifully drink it, then, following her daily telegraphed signal of sworn secrecy, wipe my mouth with the back of my hand to hide the evidence. I hasten back to brag some more: "And guess wha, guess wha."

In unison: "Wha?"

"Maas Aaron tell me say him goat have kid."

"When dat?" Exclaims Ackee Red.

"Him say a last night him drop."

"Laa la." Canepiece Rat unfolds a mystery.

"A wha?" Ackee Red and I question in unison:

"If the goat have kid before day!"

Ackee Red is impatient: "Wha dat say!"

"Take time wid me no man.... Youtman?"

"A no me say so."

"A ask me a ask you something man."

"Den ask no."

"A what time a the day you born?"

"Them say a half past ten the night."

"So the goat dem born on you birthday."

"Yes."

"So goat head the birthday list today!"

"Yes."

"And you bring us the news!"

105

"Me no understand what you mean."

"You no get it?" He asks with a wry smile.

"No."

"Me neither," adds Ackee Red.

"Yu birthday, Goat Head, a new name!"

Mystified I ask: "What that?"

"Goathead."

I know better but: "A who you a call Goathead? Renk?"

Bad move.

* * *

Mama's expertise at preparing five star chef-like meals out of almost nothing is demonstrated again this morning. Pregnant with anticipation, I rush my grace: "Fatherwethankyouforthisthatthouhastprovided praythatyousanctifyandblessitforthenourishmentofour bodiesinJesusnameamen."

Translation: "Father we thank you for this that Thou hast provided Pray that You sanctify and bless it for the nourishment of our bodies In Jesus' name. Amen." My prayer, combined with the aroma of the breakfast also attracts the cats, dogs and fowls to gather round, mainly at Dada's feet, as he seems to give them everything on the table. Mama outdoes herself again this morning. Her skills around the fireside are not taken for granted as Dada, without any notice to her, invites friends and strangers alike to join him for meals. Meals for which they are always highly appreciative and can never cease to positively compliment Mama on. But they are never to Dada's satisfaction, which is perhaps one of the reasons the animals get so much: "Iris it look like you run out o' salt? You neva have no more?" That's his way of saying it's salty.

"Sorry Willie."

Too much smoke fore his liking. "Jeesaz Iris it looks like a so so smoke yu take and cook the egg?"

Not soft enough for him. "Pickney hunnu go look one hammer carry come me soften up the piece a the fry pork!" "But a so so Gad hile dis, whey de meat?" Inadequate.

"Anything you say Willie."

Not hot: "Yu run out of fire mek the food col' so?"

"One o yu go pick one scotch bonnet carry come... me add little taste to the food..."

You would think the man can boil even water without burning it, which he can't, but this is a Jamaican Man for you. Without Mama he'd probably starve, but that doesn't stop him from spouting off at the mouth.

"Ohhhh Go'." I wince, fanning my mouth, looking at Mama, glad that I hold off on taking the Lord's name in vain.

She gasps: "What's a matter!"

Dada opines: "See the boy almost burn a new throat hole with the banana pop." Then to me he suggests: "Break up you mongoose bread bump in the porridge and cocoa tea... it can start cool."

"Yes Dada." As I put his words into action. Conversation limited, I finish the porridge as soon as it is bearable. I bolt from the table trailing: "Excuse me."

But before I make it out the door Dada cautions: "Don't start to play right away boy, make you food digest first." Having attacked their breakfast with the same enthusiasm, my friends and I hit the pavement at the same time. We create nuff games to ward off boredom, a word frankly that is not in our vocabulary. Ackee Red asks: "Who ready fo a game of hop-scotch?"

"Not me, Dada say to wait till me food digest." Ackee Red asks: "Massa yu know how long dat tek?"

"No sah, but me don't backchat him!"

"Well, by de time yu food digest, bus come."

"So whe we goin to do now?"

Canepiece Rat suggests: "Make we play Statue." Just outside the shadows of the trees on the road our game begins. With our backs to the sun we stare at our shadows for a minute without blinking, burning the image onto our retinas. We then close our eyes, stare dead ahead and 'watch' our eyelids until the image fades, then do it again. After an eternity I ask: "Dada, can we go bathe now?" Ackee Red takes off to get his soap and towel. As Canepiece-Rat and I wait Gang Gang Galina shouts: "Hhoooop," it's how she calls him.

Glancing over his shoulder Ackee Red jeers: "Canepiece Rat! Bwoy yu granny ready to play hide and seek."

"Why yu no leff me granny alone," he shouts back as he dashes home. He soon returns breathless and volunteers the reason for his attention-getting call: "…Soon time for me to go look (gather) wood fo dinner…" His return reminds Dada that I'm awaiting a reply on the river issue and seeing him Dada says: "O.K. Sonny boy yu can go bathe with yu frien dem, hunnu careful, not too much rompin!"

I dash to get my soap and towel then ex the spot: "Thanks Dada, yes Dada, yes Dada, mean no Dada, we gone Dada!"

"So whe we a go bathe?": Ackee red asks.

Canepiece Rat: "Mek we bathe behind fe yu house."

"Wha mek?" Ackee Red barks back.

"Them can see we from we house if anything!"

"All right," Ackee Red says, adding; "At least me can still swim and dive in the pool!"

I pipe in: "You too show off since you learn to swim."

109

Jeering he replies: "You must learn since it so easy!"

Canepiece Rat: "Hol me nose, me dive longer dan yu."

The cold water falls swiftly through the gouge-narrowed channel. Its pressure offers excellent massages; but to enjoy the therapeutic effect, we must have a good footing on the slippery rocks, brace ourselves or be swept into the wading pool. The heavily-travelled path from Hilltop is but a stone's throw away; still, atop the rock, we casually strip to our birthday suits. Canepiece Rat and I head to the wading portion of the natural pool. Ackee Red on the other hand climbs the rock to a point above the deepest section then asks: "Who want to play shark?"

Canepiece Rat tries insults: "Boy Ackee Red yu too braggadocios fo yu own good! Yu know a'ready say we can't swim so wha yu a do? Try fe shame we?"

I hiss my teeth at Ackee Red then compliment Canepiece Rat's statement: "Mek old show off go on... mek we hold our nose and see who can hold them breath the longest?"

With a big splash he dives in: "Geronimooooooooo!"

Soon our teeth begin to chatter but we continue playing. Seeming like about an hour later, Canepiece Rat looking at his hands exclaim: "Me hands start to shrivel!" Just then his grandmother appears on the

110

river's bank, he adds: "See Gang Gang come fe me...
and Youtman have to go get ready!"

"Yes and me body start turn ashes white!"

"Guess we better soap up, wash off and leave..."
Gang Gang Galina: "How much time me must tell yu
fe soap up before yu start play boy!"
Canepiece Rat gives her his pat answer: "Yu won't
have fe tell me again Gang Gang."

"Yu say that every time boy... boy me can't
bother wid yu yu kno... if two minute pass and yu
don't reach home? Me and yu..." She adds as she
departs.

"Youtman make haste lend me the soap..."

"Wait man... yu never have soap yet."
After a big splash Ackee Red walks out of the pool and
straight into his clothes: "Me first finish and me not
even going anywhere!"
I step into my clothes; teeth still chattering: "So, so
what yu wa want... first prize?"
Canepiece Rat chimes in: "If me never have to wait
pon the soap me would finish long time!"
Ackee Red becomes the salesman: "Then bring yu own
nex time... soap sell a me shop."
Canepiece Rat criticizes my skin; comments: "Laa la...
look how Youtman start dry up and look like ashes
Pompeii!" A phenomenon that is more visible on the

both of us than on Ackee Red, with his lighter complexion. But it's nothing copious amounts of coconut oil, the rural skin lotion, won't cure.

My hands and feet are reflecting like the shiny chrome handlebars on Sancho Panza, the telegram deliverer's bicycle. Mama puts some oil onto my close-cropped hair and with a rigid hairbrush capable of currycombing a horse she removes some of my scalp. I wince and she commands: "Boy stan tudy no."
Maas Teetie stops by in his boas'y motorcar to pick up his suit: "Mawnin Tailah, Miss Iris."

"Hey blood how you do?"

"A pleasant morning sar."

"And to you too Miss Iris."

"How the suit Tailah?"

"As me promise." Then he proudly adds: "A me granboy birthday today you know."

"A so sah? Come me boy... here, buy one sweetie!"

I'm ecstatic: "Thank yu sah."
Dressed, Mama sits on a bench on the piazza: "Sonny come stay right here," she points to the sag in the front of her dress, just north of her knees. Once I'm corralled she loosely intertwines her fingers and thumbs curtailing my gleeful prancing.

Chapter Seven

HEARING ELEVEN O'CLOCK BUS TRUMPET ITS approach, I almost jump from Mama's lap, she remarks, "Tan tudy nuh!" My heart races I bid a breathless adieu: "Me gone Dada, me gone Rev." And to a current apprentice: "Me gawn Sidges."

Dada reprimands: "Yu sure yu not forgetting yu manners?"

"Me gone Maas Teetie!"

"Walk good me boy…." The colloquialisism is lost on me: "A bus we a tek sah!"

113

Me know me boy… me know….”
Dada puts a shilling into my hand with a, “Here Sonny, tek dis and buy sup’m when yu gaa Spaalin’ heary?”

“Yes Dada. Thank yu Dada!”
Mama wears a white hat with two inches of netting. Clutching a white patent leather purse she asks: “How me look Willie?”
Maas Teetie responds: “Yu look as nice as nine pence!”

“Teetie yu tek the words right out of me mouth!”

“Had dem fe a while Willie. Yu nuh use them?”

“Iris, there is a time and place for everything.”

“Yu right Willie… me jus a mout yu… me gone…” Crossing the road, with me in tow, she flags down the bus. Systematically working his magic, with the engine, transmission, brake, clutch and gas pedals, Canute brings the bus to a stop. Mama avoids the head-on body slam of the behemoths marl-carrying wake currents by turning her body westward. I do the same. The bus stops with its curbside front tyre close to us.

Mama protects her innards from the assault by placing her hanky over her mouth and nostrils. The warm marl dust bathes me in the alluring aroma of the internal combustion engine’s by-products and I inhale an exhilarating lungful: A mix of hot convection gases, spent diesel fuel from a leaky exhaust manifold and fifty-weight oil from one bank of the leaky valve cover gasket. My nostrils resemble those of someone on a serious 'nose-candy' binge. The coconut oil on my body takes hostage more particles than the law allows. My wounded scalp attracts half-pound of marl. The dust in my eyes dissolves. Everything is everything. Everything's copasetic. Everything cook and curry.

She swings me ahead of her aboard the bus; I half climb, half levitate the three-rung wooden steps as convex lenses peer from behind disc-shaped wire lattices on either side of the middle rung. A red plaque on the third rung, having recessed, white scripted block letters, warns: "WATCH YOUR STEP."

In the centre aisle I glance to my right, onto a sea of faces progressively obscured by the chrome handrails atop the seatbacks. Above their heads, close to the ceiling, running the length of the passenger compartment, are open shelves, the storage area for carry-on luggage. Above the internal rear-view mirror a sign warns,

"PLEASE KEEP YOUR HANDS AND HEAD INSIDE."

Another informs,

"SEATING CAPACITY 45 STANDING CAPACITY 44."

There is space for one on the sideways' seat opposite the driver. Conversations among teenage boys make it clear that the sideways seat is the one for serious gear-heads. Mentally I'm already there. A quick glance up at Mama seeks to confirm the physical. She responds silently: A warm smile and a nod and my body's heading there. Two man-sized red palms imprinted atop the metal hump of the engine's nacelle precede,

"KEEP YOUR HANDS OFF. HOT."

I steer clear of it.

The seat is in the cockpit area. Unlike the passenger compartment, its wooden floorboards are covered with the shiny, slippery sheet metal used to make the bus' exterior. I gingerly cross the separating hump to take my seat. Coincidentally, the two men sitting here are a driver and mechanic on their way to retrieve a disabled bus. They exchange knowing glances and yield the up front portion of the seat to me. As I sit, the gentleman, the driver, nearest to me says: "Son, I can see you're delighted to sit up here!"

"Yes sah!" I reply.

As I wiggle aboard the seat, Canute, the driver who sits atop a height-adjustable centre pole, is given the 'all-clear'--quick succession of three wooden-sounding thuds-- by the sideman, standing by the rear door but monitoring our activity through the clear Plexiglass above the heads of the seated curb-side passengers, followed by: "Go-so-bus."

I am mesmerized by what I envision as the best thing this side of the Pearly Gates. Canute doesn't hesitate with the lesson's delivery. A quick tug on the horn's silvery chain, which is hinged to the jamb of his personal entry/exit door, produces a "Pra-mam;" it declares his intent to get rolling. He checks his mirrors, grasps the seemingly late stage Parkinson's disease suffering gear-stick, which, when in neutral and under no load from the drive train gyrates in a long lazy arc over the dome of the engine bay, rocking, like a hasty pendulum, to the grr grr grr idle of the massive diesel. The local diesel engine groupies with unverifiable automotive knowledge, in feeding their egos concur that regardless of the driver, there is no greater automotive experience, than being a pedestrian observer to this particular activity. Mongoose and his uncle, Driver, are currently vying for the local chapter's presidency, and if their apparent knowledge base is taken into consideration, then they should co-chair the club. It was two Saturdays ago, they were talking…

Mongoose: "Man, mek me tell yu, when any driver walk thru the box properly! It can send chill down the spine of a worm me a tell yu!"

Driver: " Worm have spine boy! Or yu a idiot?"

"Uncle man me jus a mek a point!"

"Mek yu point Worm Spine."

"Even if yu one mile away! A still music."

"True yu can still hear a driver 'walking' through a mated gearbox but yu miss some of the things..."

"No sah yu don't miss a thing!"

"Mongoose, me not askin yu? Me telling yu!"

"Awright... what me miss if me far?"

"Me can't name all o them, but yu miss nuff." Indeed. Aboard the bus every intake, compression, power and exhaust stroke is transmitted up through the chassis, the seat and into my entire being. The dynamic transitions send shockwaves through my body, giving me a full body massage. Unaware that I am temporarily blocking Canute's view, I expertly use the left side wing mirror, I watch the tail of the curbside-trailing dust cloud and can only imagine the street side exhaust pipe: Thick belching black smoke of spent fuel every time Canute dumps the clutch. I am in awe of the dust free cabin.

Some say, this sensation can't be beat. I'm currently too swayed to argue. Those in the know, though, will argue the pros and cons of the different continents' diesels with superchargers and turbochargers, screws and twin screws. Well, hooray for them but they aren't sitting on a slippery, wrong direction facing, overstuffed vinyl bench across from Canute for seventy-leven miles of bad road. The engine is tickling my tympanic with the most melodious music. This, for the moment includes ska. The din of its enchantingly raspy air intake, laborious hydraulic lifters timing the compression, whining rubber belts, chain driven connections on the power stroke, the calamitous racket of spent gases on the exhaust, the dance of mating straight cut cogs in the gearbox on a clutch-less shift, the consequential rumble of the chassis from the undamped harmonics fed up through the leaf springs from the live axle connected, inner-tube sporting, hard riding pneumatic tires, to the metal chassis 'U' clamped to the wooden frame rumbles into the passenger compartment and rattles the square cut Plexiglas shields in their hinged window boxes, bounces the wooden window flaps and closely spaced floorboards. The rattling metal clasps on the engine's nacelle cover causes me, a small example of the tropically primed testosterone male, to reword scripture, make it read like poetry. Make it read like…

I lifteth my ears onto the turmoil
From whence drivetrain motions cometh in oil

Dozens of gearbox cogs meshing
Rearward the power sending

From the engine fan's cooling
To the pressure plate's throwout bearing

The unsapped torque to coupled drive shafts
The axle's helical cogs, drive wheels half shafts

After which cometh the motivation
Beginning its final rotation
Insisting to the axle's spider gears
Never quit spooling the power to the rears
Of all music this one brings me closest to tears
But please Lord don't get me wrong
Oh no they'd be tears for a joyous song

None of us boys locally
Be it sober, drunk or on Callie
Overstands the first thing about a tranny

Though technically speaking we are off the mark
We really care not if we ever get it out of park

All we really want to do
King-man is go on like we really really know
That's why we demonstrate so much bravado

Amen

My fellow gear heads are not here to see him feather the clutch in first, side step it in second and disregard it from then on. To follow him out of the range of a stationary earshot, listen to him saw his way towards the diesel car's twelve hundred revolutions per minute governor with stabs and partial releases of the accelerator pedal. Rowing through the shift pattern, seeing the statuesque leanings of a gearshift lever under load, making use of the full range of the dual gears which are actuated by the in/out toggle action on the small red flute shaped knob atop the metal-tube shielded in spirally wound steel cables that parallel the gearshift lever's arc down to the transmission tunnel then running out of sight to the axles in the rear; the actions of his feet are hidden from my view but his body English betrays serious activity south of his thighs as he briefly half-masts (partially depresses) the clutch bringing new ratios into play; propelling the bus with a whopping one-to-two miles per hour increase in forward speed, to hear the din rise to a crescendo, to pick up, though unsure what to do with the subtleties in the groans of engine as it speaks to load dependent gear ratios; wailing a different tune! For a boy! Any boy in my neck of the woods! Anywhere on The Rock; to hear this is to be pronounced dead, done dead, done, died and gone to heaven, enginelulah.

My seatmate talks over the din of the engine: "So where are you going little man?"

"Is my birthday sar, me granny taking me...!"

"I see... that is her over there?"

"Yes sah."

"So how come yu didn't sit with her?"

"Me want to see everyting the driver doing sah."

"Suppose I tell you that you are in luck today!"

"How sah!"

Pointing he says: "You see the driver?"

"Yes sah."

"I taught him everything he knows!"

"A true sah?"

"Yes it is... I used to be a driver like him before I went away to study..."

"Study sah?"

"Yes I study mechanical engineering..."

"What is that sah?"

"To make a long story short it helps me to now build the busses that other people drive..."

"A you build this one sah?"

"Yes... with the help of my staff...."

"Teachers sah?"

"Noooo heh heh good heavens no... carpenters, welders, mechanics and other trades people..."

"Plenty people sah?"

"Yes. Work hard in school… you can do it too…"

"Yes sah…"

"I'm going to explain everything he does…"

Canute is now in fifth low. Through the windshield and windows to his right, the town blurs by at ten miles per hour. Air entering the cabin through the infinitely adjustable, open rectangular slot below the windshield body-slams my eyes, force tears towards my ears as they dutifully report the competing engine melodies and the basso ruffling sounds of mighty rushing winds to my brain. In a true left-brain, right-brain test, the wind is raisin' cane in my left ear, while the right is able to absorb things mechanical. The speed is so ferocious that there is not even one dead bug across the entire acre of glass in front of us. Not one post-larvae fly. Not one post chrysalis butterfly. Not a housefly. Sourfly. Sand fly. Horsefly. No gingie fly. Not a wasp. Not a gal-a-wasp. No mosquito. Not one needle-case at the end of its metamorphosis. Not one moth. Not one kapay/peenie wally. Not one fiddler beetle. Not a tumble tud. Not a maybug. Not a june bug. Not one news-bug. Chinch bug. Not a bed bug.

From standstill, we travel less than a quarter mile and the silent till-tomorrow's hand-clapping, foot-stomping Church of God on the hill at the far end of town comes into view. We're flat flyin'. Twelve miles per hour. Bird speed. Ahead, a Higgler's hand reaches out, pats the air like a circling Johncrow's wing; Canute responds by bringing his mechanical steed to a stop at their feet. Bredda Man loads their assorted leaf and scraps-tagged crocus bags in the carrier atop the bus, further increasing the already high centre of gravity. Soon we're off again.

I can't believe my ears: "Wait till I tell Canepiece Rat and Ackee Red about this!"

"Tell who?"

"My friends sah!"

"I had a nickname while growing up! I can just picture your friends by their names... what's yours?"

"Youtman sah!"

"Does that mean what I think it means?"

"A don't know what yu thinking sah!"

"Youth-man! Youth of a man Youtman is it?"

"Yes sah... that is it!"

"Who gave you that name?"

"Me uncle Cinco sah."

"I see... I had one growing up too..."

"Yes sah!"

"Want to know what it is?"

"Yes sah!"

"Buzzy!"

"A true sah!"

YOUTMAN Saturday's Child

"Why do you think that is?"

"A don't know sah!"

"I used to be as busy as a bee... ran everywhere... making a sound like an engine that my friends said sounded more like a honey bee..."

"Well tell you what... because you remind me so much of me! I want you to call me that... O.K?"

"Yes sah."

"So what's my name?"

"Missa Buzzy sah."

"Ha ha ha... that's good..."

Pitch and Tar, the paved 'S' bend approaches. Canute's bony wrists protrude beneath the multicoloured plaid cuff. His big vicelike knuckles grip the steering wheel one moment then the gearshift the next. Three triple sets of bicycle spokes-like rods go outward from the hub to the three, six and nine o'clock positions. For now, he steers with his right hand at three o'clock; his left is busy with the gear selecting. Now the 'S'. Canute unmasks his work face, mouth twisted to one side. Briefly disregarding the gear stick, he steers with his left hand, reaches towards the window jamb to his right, grasps a silver chain, a dangling lowercase 'j' stemming from between the compressed air pressure release valve at its anchor and jerks it in an arcing rhythmic cadence. The air it releases through the air-horns atop the bus produce his signature "A pretty gal me want, a pretty, pretty, pretty gal me want." To the seasoned passenger the situation, I'm sure, would seem normal. I, however, am guilty of a seeming S.N.A.F.U. (situation normal all f----d up)

In the headlong rush the bus appears to demolish everything thirty feet ahead of its front bumper. We seem to be off the road, over battery, cutting an invisible and unencumbered swath through momentum sapping, progress terminating, mature orange trees. As we soar through the branches, he manipulates the large steering wheel, quickly circling its mass with his brawny hands. Once. Then rapidly pulling; on its right side; hand over hand; in well schooled and well executed motions; he frantically works to change the beast's direction.

Missa Buzzy is sitting here thinking: The engine's bogging down in revolutions. Holding the steering arc for a moment with the right, he punches in the dual and depresses the clutch briefly but this new ratio's power is quickly sapped so he snatches the gear lever, depresses the clutch, crosses the gate and draws one lower in the box, simultaneously resets the dual to the high out position and dumps the clutch... and then, over the din of the engine, he wonders aloud: "How much of this are you getting?"

"A trying to take in the whole thing sah!"

The implication of Canute's name (Can do youth) becomes self evident as he rises out of the seat and grasps the wheel with his left at one o'clock continuing the pull to four o'clock while readying his right to begin its one to four shift. We soar like a bird, heading towards the road.

"You are in luck today Youtman!"

"Why yu say that sah?"

"Well first, you never told me where you going?"

"Spaalin sah."

"Well, by the time you get there!"

"Yes sah…"

"You will be the smartest little boy on the bus."

"Thank yu sah!"

The decreasing corner radius scrubs more speed, the increasing inclines bring additional load, the diesel car talks, the engine bogs and Canute's ready. Maintaining his semi standing posture, he swiftly kicks the clutch to activate the pre-selected dual gear. He massages the accelerator; increasing the engine R.P.M.'s, the engine responds. Music. The other side of the bend beckons, impatiently. Now the horn. Now the gear selection. The wheel. It's up on the dual button and a lower gear. On it's the apparent overshoot of the other side of the road, we slam into the culvert. The lack of damage confounds at least one passenger.

I'm mesmerised; all sorts of thoughts race through my mind: What kind of driving is this today? Kiss me back foot! Has he lost it all? The first time I have a chance to go someplace on the bus, and he's taking up the whole road.

Missa Buzzy reads my mind: "The driver is reading the road Youtman."

"Doing what sah?"

"By glancing ahead looking for clouds of dust…"

"Why him do that Missa Buzzy?"

"You see son… to the casual observer the trail means nothing…"

"Then why him do it sah?"

"Patience Youtman!"

"Sorry sah."

"The dust trail betrays that vehicle's approximate speed and even its size…"

Quizzically I agree: "I see…"

Seeing my dilemma he continues, further complicating matters: "Familiarity with the terrain's serpentine layout will reveal its true direction."

"What sah."

"Watching the dust trail on the hill he can tell which way the vehicle is going but, of course, all this expertise is drowned with the first shower of rain."

Public conveyance pickup points are a separate science. Those in front of shops and at intersections are expected. Others are a hundred miles from nowhere. The underbrush quickly swallows up a foot track now intersecting the road. Grand entranceways such as this may lead to the residences of many families.

I tear my eyes away from the motivator's excitement to stare bug-eyed across the aisle at Mama and she nods with an understanding smile. Canute is enjoying the respite of a brief plateau, no gradient reducing corners; he selects higher and higher gears. We hurtle towards sixteen miles per hour. Partially exposed root systems of precariously hanging trees protrude from the hills on his side while treetops offer a valley's panorama on mine. We hurtle towards a hairpin that climbs on exit. Clumps of bamboos jut from the embankment in front of the citrus waving a threat at the external paintjob and the wayward limbs of any half-crazy or illiterate passenger who disobeys the warning: "PLEASE KEEP YOUR HANDS AND HEAD INSIDE."

As we continue the serpentine climb, we often reverse direction bringing about changes in the foreground scenery the passengers sitting on the opposite side now unwittingly risk limb-dismemberment by the precarious overhangs and protruding roots. The conductress makes her way to Mama who mouths 'Spaulding' --the proper name of our destination-- and indicates that there are two of us, then points to me. I tear myself away from Canute's performance long enough to recognize the manicured embankments and stone retention walls on portions of the road my shortcuts eliminate.

Chapter Eight

BEYOND THE KNIGHTENGALE'S PROPERTY, the terrain grows harsher. Maas Aaron; a frozen wave, a frozen grin, the mouthing of something: Me goat got kid! Bad Rock is scary. Painted, one-room, mansions with rusting rooftops punctuate the landscape. Peaks rise below us. Precipices cascade into valleys. Tracks disappear over precipices. On the ascending side of the road, scant soil exposes Fold Mountains and pathways that quickly disappear above the roof of the bus. Robust vines of Sain' Vincen', Barby, Yellow and

Haffu yams cover bamboo sticks. Prosperous roadside residences are interspersed among the mere shelters. Our pilot negotiates a tight lefthander that climbs a steep grade; a hand reaches out and flags him down. New to Higglering, the sideman cautions her about miraculously averted, calamities she poses by placing loads curbside, in the middle of a bends. The baggage: crocus bags made from jute. This one full of jelly coconuts, that one dry coconuts, with oranges, yams, cocoe, dasheen, chocho, breadfruit and ackee... Bredda-man scampers up the rear-mounted ladder and clambers down the curbside extension above the windows then grasps the strength-demanding higgler-slung bags and places them in the carrier. We're off again, "go-so-bus." An unpainted cement shop glides by in the panorama of a wide corner. The parochial road next to it suggests a district or two beyond the intersection.

We crest the first gear hill onto the plateau and suddenly the two-parish town of Spaulding looms into view. The road is paved so we lose some of the harmonics. We are enveloped in briskly circulating air with the increased road speed. Humanity forms a black sea. Canute is about to wake the town and tell the people he has a musical bus coming their way. The engine's revolutions climb as we approach three miles per hour. He kicks the clutch to actuate overdrive second gear as we ease by the two-story police station. Selecting third gear now, the dual pushed in, he kicks the clutch, dual out, clutch, overdrive fourth, a smattering of single story residences wisp by. Now upscale residences, set back from the roadway behind hibiscus and croton fences, at the end of long driveways, fly by. I've never seen this many cars, trucks, busses or people. Fifth, clutch, and our acceleration is equivalent to that of an un-saddled ginny jackass at full gallop. It's definitely as fast as this body has ever been flung through space. Missa Buzzy taps my shoulder, and begins speaking: "Now Youtman all the stops you have seen so far! Cannot compare to this."

"What yu mean sah?"

"The boys... live for moments like this... hear Canute do his thing... watch him operate..."

We fly towards the 'T' junction where the finger post stuck in a banana yellow, two yards wide, ramping from the initial four to eight inches cement base, is the centre of the street at town centre. Our cruising speed is now twenty-two miles per hour. I know everything there is to know about driving this bus now, and will have no problem driving if something, as I am desperately hoping, happens to Canute. City centre approaches under a bouncy speedometer's, fluctuating indication of fifteen to forty-five miles per hour.

In every town, a posse of alert youth-massive, with banana-cutting appendages waits for the operator of any mechanical contrivance willing to perform. In so doing, he demonstrates his automotive acumen, captivates his audience, and at the end of the performance, he can walk away a celebrity.

To show how him wicked --this is a good thing-- he must bring his transport to a stop, with either minimal use of, or zero brakes. When applied their forceful expulsion of compressed air will be a dead give-a-way. Their use, will work against him in the skill department, when judged against the best of the best, dark-skinned only, exclusive club operators; people like Fleet Foot, Gryah the meagre Indian and the legendary Tipper Fire.

In full sight of the masses he sounds the horn, "A pretty gal me want...." Stiffening his arms at six o'clock he pushes himself back from the steering wheel. Sitting erect, he stabs the brakes: May I have your attention please. His left hand tracks, locates and encapsulates the Parkinson's gearshift knob within the confines of a half fist; his little finger is bent on playing target practice with the engine's nacelle. At half the normal rate, he coaxes the accelerator pedal towards the floor, punches in the dual with his thumb and stiff-arms the steering with his right hand at the five o'clock position and kicks the clutch. The engine responds to the race-change causing him to stick his tongue out and massage his Afro-centric lips. He stabs the brake pedal; the compressed air's hiss travels to all the ears in the impromptu court, speaks to all interested parties.

The audience figures its use adds to the performance. Some daredevils stand on the finger post, blocking the sign for the few unfamiliar motorists.

He kicks the clutch pedal. The engine responds with a change in tune and the revolutions per minute (revs) climb to fourteen hundred. Passengers standing in the aisle sway to the limit of their torso's and arms. As the revs fall the bus decelerates, both road and engine speeds become of such proportions as to cause minimal pressure onto the teeth of the meshed gears. They disengage easily when, without the use of the clutch, he slips the lever into neutral. He rocks the gearshift lever in a wrist-limiting side-to-side motion and identifies the gate position where the left-pulling spring caresses the reverse lockout detent at the far side of the 'H' pattern. Gas, clutch, applied simultaneously with both feet. He guides the lever across a single detent in the gate, then hauls it upwards into fourth and sidesteps the clutch --removes his foot by slipping it to the side thus allowing the clutch to return to its home position aided only by the constant pressure of the springs on the pressure plate.

The seated passengers all bow, except the three of us on my seat; we kind'a slide sideways. I'm almost off the seat.

Heel and toe --simultaneously depressing the clutch, brake and gas pedals-- neutral and dual, gas, up clutch, down clutch, gear, gas, up clutch, gas release and engine solo, acapella compression, punch in the dual, kick the clutch, stab the gas, let it go, let-it-go. Music. I die today.

I am in bus heaven, intoxicated with the rhythm. On queue I rock sideways, to the left, the seated passengers nod and the standing ones sway. I can do this all day. As I recoil, then steady to the right the seated simultaneously raise their heads as if after a prayer's amen. He floors the gas and clutch pedals simultaneously and hauls the gearshift lever upwards and, as if it suddenly became unbearably hot, he quickly releases it, his arm flailing upwards, wrist leading fingers spread to allow the maximum airflow of the high altitude cooler air entering the cabin through the horizontal vents under the windshield to go through them, sidesteps the clutch and jumps off the accelerator pedal, the engine whines and the bus attempts to stop, but is forced forward by the momentum, I feel myself being shoved out the windshield by an invisible force I do not understand. As the seated passengers all bow, the standing sway to the limit of their combined arms again. He stabs the brake, jabs the gas pedal allowing the bus to briefly attempt acceleration, then he kicks the clutch allowing the engine to briefly race towards its governor and releases the gas. The dual now selecting a lower final drive ratio induces more compression that incrementally retards our forward progress again. He locates the shifter and backhands it into neutral, gives her a couple of motivationally useless but musically priceless stabs on the accelerator. Palm forward, pulls out the dual with his victory sign fingers. Palm facing down and grasping the ball atop the gear stick, he floors the clutch and gas pedals and shoves the lever definitively down into third, sidesteps the clutch and jumps off the gas again eliciting another involuntary nod from the passengers and conductress. Breddaman at his customary position, his left foot dangling freely in the air outside the open back door while his open shirt blows in the wind and myself heads in the general direction of the windshield once more but then abruptly and inexplicably stops due to the still unheard of Sir Isaac Newton's laws of motion. Now, he punches the dual in, gas/clutch, release, hhhmmmm, the engine responds with the wailing of intake, compression, power and exhaust strokes of all eight cylinders having a lot of momentum but denied the input of fuel.

The observing masses become uncorked and fling their hands in the air in unison and with eyes and teeth aglow they shout amongst themselves, "Go inna it drivah."

Neutral. Dual. Brake. Two. Dual. Orchestra. Audience. Passengers. Bredda-man. Driver. Me. Brake. Gas. Clutch. Orchestra. Dual. Audience. Passengers. Bredda-man. Driver. Me. Neutral. Brake. Clutch. Dual. One. Orchestra. Audience. Passengers. Bredda-man. Driver. Me. Gas. Clutch. Dual. Orchestra. Audience. Passengers. Driver. Bredda-man. Me. The bus attempts to stop as the R.P.M.'s reach into redlining territory but before the current mechanical actions can complete their alloy-threatening cycles, he feathers the clutch, uses his right foot to stab and release the brake then the accelerator. Under a seemingly prearranged orchestration, he deftly brings it to a stop literally on top of the receding throng. He engages the large chrome floor-mounted parking brake by pulling up and releasing it three times for it to prime and hold properly and quiets the gyrating gear selector by punching the kill switch with the side of his fist. He looks at me smiling and says, "Yu love it my Yout'!" I intend to respond, but the words cannot escape my lips. He jumps to the pavement, into the applause and back-slapping of the mobbing groupies. Missa Buzzy in a somewhat subdued voice says: "Youtman I hope you enjoyed your trip?"

"Oh yes sah... yes sah!"

"Well go take care of granny..."

Mama gives me the go sign but Broomie, is in the bus blocking the aisle. He appears to be speaking softly but he is actually yelling, "Buy you tidyness! Buy you tidyness!" The Drops lady is outside, yelling just as softly, "Grater cake, drops, drops, grater cake!" The homemade ice cream vendor, ditto, "Creamie! Shave ice! Creamie!"

All the sounds compete with the ringing in my ears.

We alight. My ears are corked and my nose is stuffy. People! I look up, at the balconies above the square and in a marked difference to my district; the verandas are populated with overhanging mallata pickneys. Mama takes a firm hold of my hand and we work our way to the east where her friend, my godmother Miss Una, works in a fabric store. I am 'the bees' knees'. Elated. This town's so big. So many people, it looks like Judgement. My ears are in dire need of decompression. So much activity: Car, bus, truck, horse and buggy, horse, mule, jackass, hog and goat, all vying for the same bit of tarmac. The mix of odours: Bagged feed for pigs and chicken; a designated urinal the other side of a sheet of zinc abuts the side of a rum bar hidden from view only, stench present: vomit and urine. Kerosene oil. Salt fish. Red herring. Ripe bananas. Humanity with over extended bath and deodorant intervals --rampant greendelero. Patties heated in the glass case. Cigar and cigarette smoke. Diesel fuel dripping from leaky tanks. Bruised produce, by the smell of it, suggest huge discount by its seller. Man's beasts of burden's indiscriminate releases. Garbage burning. Live chicken. Tobacco, uncut rope. Fry fritters. An obstructed walkway with the courtesy of a coconut drops vendor. A poorly parked car shunts people into the street.

I see a fabric-tensive store for the first time. Floor to rafters, nothing but reams of claat: gabardine, terylene, nylon, all-wool, crème serge, velvet, lace, khaki, taffetas, silk, satin and crocus bag. Colour for days. Solids, plaids, polka dots, checks, stripes, granny print, kiss me granny. Mama greets her friend: "Una gal yu look good bad."

"Iris gal, yu look hearty to! Yu look good bad."

"Lawd Missis. Tings no pretty. Mi jus a tek kin teet cover heart bu'n. Then a how yu do missis?"

"Mi Sis yu no know how it go! Where there's a will there's a way. Me have fe tenk Gad fe Jeezas wid de lickle bit o me dat leff!"

"Missis yu can say that again, Me-self, lickle bit o'me lef' bra, dey yah a blow fe life!"

"Happy birthday Youtman!"

"Thank you godmodder."

"But Iris, Willie still a make trousers out o' people cloth for the boy eh Ma!"

"But you know say Willie not goin' do less Ma!"

"Favor him a cut out for him grandchild firs'?"

"Yes mah! Christen him own pickney firs'."

"The boy own look good like customer's."

"Line up every stripe me dear mam!"

"Yu lie! 'Prentice them stayin' longer now?"

"Stay Missis? As dem lawn them gawn."

"Children them too ungrateful nowadays Ma, The Lard mus' soon come fe Him Worl'."

"So my godson?"

"Yes'n."

"You can get anything that you want to eat!" Eating being a very important part of our culture, food is one of the first things one is offered at a meeting of friends and possibly the last thing offered before one's departure. Casually glancing around the store, I order what absolutely has to be there but is just evading my mechanically overloaded eyesight so far.

"Sardine and bread."

"Whey you want to drink me son?"

I request top shelf stuff, "Cola champagne mah."
Mama looks as if she wants to change my diction.
Goddie speaks to an omni listening but invisible face in
the back of the place, "Hi… fix one can o' Sardine and
mongoose-bread for me Godson. Heary?"

"Yes'n!" Dimples, magically appears in the
connecting doorway confirming the communication,
very pretty young lady, complementing the adage, "The
blacker the berry the sweeter the juice," avoids all eye
contact with her elders as a point of respect. She comes
towards me picking an invisible thorn from her left
palm with her right thumb and forefinger, pauses in
front of me and without eye contact says to me, "Please
to fallow me sar."

I follow two thick plaits of hair, braided to
accentuate the curvature of her ear lobes. A budding
form, defined by a coating of coconut oil, leading
yesterday's frock absorbed greendelero, mixed with a
skin emitting late night bath soap, puberty defining,
customary underarm hair retained scent swaying on
the wind currents. Her form defining, gravity defying,
rolling Grotto bread, still rising, as she is not yet of age
to use up all the baking powder derriere's rivalling loaves
are a part of an art form that is artfully testing the
tapered strength of the darts from the dips of her hips
to a point midway up her sides where her arms glide

closely by in their stride to propel her meandering body to the straight ahead kitchen. Her skirt tail below, below hips on their way to bridging the gap in average doorways, appears to sway the width of the island. She has, what are in my world, the most perfectly shaped athletic calves honed on a brief academic life that necessitated serious gradient adjustments. Nurtured by years of barefoot trodding, her thick-soled foot bottom betrays a double dose of coconut oiling. This is an African thing. At the table she stops and without turning to disrupt my focus beckons me, with the back of her hand, to a chair. I sit speechless. She excuses herself and soon returns with a tray containing my big plate of sardine, hard dough bread and cola champagne. On ice. And massy me pupa, me even get the bread bump, though cut off instead of broken. Bes' Butter is to my right, in a butter dish. Bes' butter on a Saturday morning. Unheard of.

Away from management and Mama her facial countenance changes. She sits with eyes too telling for me to comprehend half of their messages, but telepathically practising just the same, scanning, meandering, purposefully roving up and down and up again eyes, eyes making and furtively maintaining eye contact eyes, sideways across from me with her hands resting on the tables edge, at the ready, with ears tailored to be attentive to the spoken and the unspoken, breathed innuendoes, in this case, in the event 'Ti Une calls her, she can be responding before the command is complete.

The plastic red and white checker tablecloth is set on the diamond with its tips touching the empty chairs sits atop one of white lace. The dark-stained stained table is visible, through the cutout slats in the lace. The plastic roses represent at table centre. She's twelve years old. Puberty paid her an early visit and left in a hurry so maturity, at least in body, could start settling in. Her lips are darker even than her very serious ebony. Her smile's a mile wide with vortex-like dimples that punctuate her cheeks. Black gums supporting perfect white teeth make a permanent impression on me. Averting my eyes from her captivating smile I look into seductive, coal black pupils below beautifully curved eyelashes. Virgin-white irises lay below thick eyebrows at the base of a flat forehead. I see, hear, sense, tense and reference sultry before I know what sultry is. She speaks, snapping me back to reality: "Me de hear that today is your birt'day. A chute?"

I swallow air like it's a rock taken with a mouthful of water: "Hhmmhhm."

"Yu don't have to jus watch me yu can eat."

"A was about to."

"If yu look down yu wi see the fork."

"Thank you." I say my grace and get a mouthful.

"Then yu de turn ho'much now?"

"Me a six tiday."

"Okay! An' yu still so little?"

She watches me eat, seemingly bemused, in silence. I break the ice. Compliments: You fix the sardines good!

"Thanks."

To dominate the situation I emulate my idol who, I'm sure, would be a master at this game; I run Dada's lists of criticisms through my mind, as I need to say something to define my manhood without belittling her, not something Dada always practices with Mama.

"The sardine taste good! Yu have any pepper?"

"Ya man me have pepper."

"Pepper come in plenty kind...what yu have?"

"Pick-A-Pepper, bird pepper, Scotch Bonnet..."

"Oh, yu have a pepper factory!"

"Ti Une love pepper with everything she eat..."

"Can have a piece of the Scotch Bonnet please!"

"It hot you kno'!"

"Hot to you but me, me eat it all the time."

"All right master, me go pick one, soon come."

Pain brings me back to reality when I accidentally bite my tongue as I watch her leave. Slowly.

"See it here, but careful yu kno them hot bad."

"Thanks."

I'm an expert at knife and fork usage thanks to Mama's tutelage; I cut about what I remember Dada cuts when he requests one, dissect that, and place a piece in my mouth with my next bit of sardine. The first place it seeks out is the deepest groove in my teeth. I expertly remove it with my tongue but this causes a lot of my juiced up saliva to flow into the groove I bit into my tongue. As the world catches fire I add a piece of bread to my mouthful, my racing mind rationalizes: this should spread things out! Dilute it to a form! But the forest fire it leaves in my drowning mouth is spreading rapidly. I swallow. I swallow. My side of the room is now in a kitchen made of bamboo wattle that is burning down and there isn't a kerosene pan of water in sight. I am caught in a trap. The door is blocked. I cry tears without an emotional trigger, snot-nose style. They hurt; they hurt my pride more than the bonfire in my mouth. I must contain the embarrassment and compose myself; to this end I have some swishy aerated water. It only serves as direct replenishment to my pores and tear ducts. I sweat and cry aerated water. Aerated water runs down my face, out my nose, out my pores like perspiration, down my forehead like sweat. Big, big embarrassment. I avoid eye contact with Miss World, add some butter quickly to another piece of bread and trying to remain calm take some sardine from as far away from the remaining piece of pepper as possible and chew on it, quickly adding a sip of my drink with a bit of the ice. My head, face and shirt feel like I'm either running cross-country or just stepped out of the river water. Except that instead of shivering, the water is warmer, body temperature. My armpits are leaky faucets. Throughout my crisis, there is uninterrupted silence from the half of the kitchen slash dining room that is yet to be ignited by the blazing fire. Cool as a cucumber on a winter morning in Mandeville, the girl I am dying to impress expresses her consciousness: "The peppers hot don't?"

I unapologetically snort snot. Swallow to clear my throat then attempt a cool comeback, one I cannot yet put to words, but will, soon as the heat on the right lobe of my brain and the fire raging on the earlobe attached to this side of my head is rid of its conflagration and the smoke and ashes clears from what has to be a barbeque to rival any that takes place over the hottest wood-fire supported creng-creng from which an unlucky piece of meat falls into the exposed crematorium of raging guava wood and bamboo root. I take too long.

The perceptive woman, "Can't say me never tell yu!"

"Whe yu a say! It no so bad!"

I'm suffering from overcomitis, and the damsel I oh so adore refuses to let up.

147

"So why yu a cry.

Why yu nose no dry

Why you a sweat like rain from the sky

Yu want piece a serviette!

Or a baby plate

Or to use yu face and wipe yu school slate

Or a nappy to dry yu perspirate!"

"Yes thanks (snort)... use it fe wipe me face."

Thanks to which one?"

"Anything... anyone o them..."

Commenting, she hands me a serviette: "Yu nose still a run, yu yeye to!"

"Yea! Yu have fe gi me piece more fe do that."

She hands me some more paper napkins.

She inveigles me: "Talk the chuth!"

"Chuth bout wha?"

"Bout the peppa man!"

Snorting half my brains back into my head: "It wicked bad. Me no want no more of it."

"You never eat pepper yet?"

"Sometime when me grandfather eating me taste a little bit of his own but it never taste like this!"

"The piece yu take too big man! Me did know."

"Then why you never say nothing to me...."

"No you a de man!"

"Wha dat suppose to mean?"

"No you a try fe impress me!" She rubs it in for effect, and with an upward toss of her head adds: "No so!" She has all the lines down pat. I want to be this smooth when my sinuses stop oozing relief, "I'm impressed!" She adds, "Is that what you want me to say?"

"No sah! Beg you piece more a the serviette." She gives me a napkin and I wipe the running perspiration starting with my forehead. I have to get as much of the sardine and bread to accompany the piece of pepper in my stomach as is possible so I'm not really into mincing words right now. Sensing my dilemma, she takes pity on me and considers changes the line of attack and switches gears entirely.

Digressing she asks, "So a you nummo as a pickney lib with yu granny?"

"No sah." Comes out of my last mouthful.

"Den a how much a hunnu de dere wid har?"

"Six o' we deh de, a me one fe call them sup'm."

"Oh. A me one 'Ti Une take. Me is not fe her children you kno'? Me is for her sister."

"Half sister or full sister?"

"Half, on me mother side."

I think: Well, you are the black sheep all right.

She clears the air, "'Ti Une take the look and colour from her Pupa, one of the Aaronn's."

149

Terrence R. E. Burey

Goddie has more milk in her coffee than the damsel under focous but being the young diplomat I am and trying to recover in my fall from grace I voice: "Yu lie. An' nearly most me ask you a how much o' hunnu lovley children she have?"

"No sah, Gad truth. A tek she tek me."

"So a whish-art you come from?"

"Belcaris. You know a whe' part that de?"

"No brah. The road bad fe go there?"

"Bad like you a go a hell."

"Yu go deh a'ready?"

"Cho, yu know wha me mean!"

"Me know, me jus a tess yu."

"Nearly most me believe yu."

"Yea nearly most. How much bus you take?"

"Two deggae deggae one!"

"Really!"

"The first one ordinary buses, but the second one-lickle bit an always pack up with all kind of things."

"So a how long it take you?"

"It a good five ower fe reach deh."

"People from there come to this market too?"

"Yes! Them put together and hire one truck…"

"Oh."

"Me see say you stop eat. Yu belly full?"

"Full of pepper!"

"You know, them have a ol' time sayin dat say 'Before good food waste, mek belly buss,' but a will excuse yu if yu stop... no tek the chance with more of the pepper."

I'm not sure how to thank her for being so understanding: "Mama use that sayin' all the time..."

"Well since as yu done, mek me show you which part you can wash your han' dem."

She escorts me to the standpipe and cistern out back. Just like down at school the foot high square cistern is designed to trap and drain the wash water, saving the area around the pipe from getting soggy. I wash my hands and mouth. She hands me a towel. The landscape suggests semi-typical district life; stand-alone kitchens, clotheslines, pails and chimmeys washed turn down to dry on big stones said speed. The barbecue on which pimento, chocolate, coffee and ginger are dried is absent though, that's the semi in it. City life! Across a valley, in the distance, an acre of the hillside, cleared of all vegetation, has given up its natural slope to be cemented. Just below it, is a huge circular concrete drum pan. I say drum pan because it has the same basic proportions only on a much larger scale. Pointing to it I ask, "A wha' dat?"

"The correc' name for it is a Catchment Area."

"Wha it a catch?"

"Water."

"Water!"

"Rain water. Mek me tell you how it work."

"Gwaan tru nuh."

"Wen time rain a fall! The rain water run off of the flat part and drain into the tank bottom side it."

"You mean the big ol' roun' sup'm bottom side it! A it a de tank?"

"A dat me say yes."

"Then a who need so much water?"

"It pipe round the whole place. Everybody's yard and the 'oospital."

"A-oh bra-bas. When no rain no fall we get fe we watah from river and drinking water from spring."

"We topside river head, we no have no river."

"Hunnu no have no river?"

"Ti Une say dis a de only parish without one."

"So where you bathe?" I ask with a broad smile.

"Yu mine whe yu a tink, me can read mind!"

"Yu too lie, whe me did a tink?"

"Me no haffy tell yu, me ketch yu areddy."

"Sorry…"

"You see the zinc wall and zinc top building!" She says pointing, "Is in there me shower."

"How you do that?"

"Make me show you"

"You mean we a go bathe?"

"But you think you no bright!"

"So what you mean?"

"Me just want to show you the bathroom."

"Then you should just say so."

"See it here."

"Then what hunnu do when no rain no fall!"

"A truck carry watah come here that time."

"Sometime so-so God air come out o de pipe?"

"A dat me de say yes."

I return the towel and display my educational ability...

"We have a spring. Me just can't understand how water just start run out of the ground like that... we have one that Mama get drinking water from but me don't understand."

"You never study that a school!"

"No..."

"Teacher say that a when the water soak through the dirt to the underground rock and they can't hold no more it start to run out like the little spring and as it go further and further more and more spring join together, it turn into river."

"Well if a so teacher say then a so it go." The cast in her eyes suggests we go indoors. Due in no small part to the inferno in my mouth, I run out of options in the dining area and suggest, "Well me a go back roun' a front to Mama and Goddie before them wonder whey we doing."

"Yu sure we have to go back already man?"

"Yes, Goddie mus have other tings fe do…"

"By the way… yu satisfy wid everything?"

"Yes man. Even the pepper."

Mama has her purchases folded and is ready.

"Take dis and buy you sweetie my son."

"T'ank you mam."

Mama rolls her eyes, "Say t'ank yu Gadmadda boy!" I oblige.

"Tell Willie a haughty howdy. God go wid yu."

"God spare we life wi' see we one anneda again!"

"Yes me dear God willin. Walk good."

I glance at the doorway. A sultry Dimples is leaning against it. Our eyes meet. Synergy. We rejoin the mayhem.

Chapter Nine

THE DIN OF PROGRESS INDICATIVE ENGINES in Milk Truck, Gleaner Car, Market Truck, Bread Van, Robot, Taxi, Royal Mail Van finishing its half day Jamaica time rounds at 1:30 p.m.; country busses galore. Cars among pedestrians round the fingerpost and shunt all the timid pedestrians into the alleyways. The occasional horse, jackass, mule and pushcart passes us without incident.

At the market Mama visits with women from our district; Miss Pinnie greets: "Hi Aunt how yu do?"

"Me blowin fe life… thank The Lord, how yu?"

"No too bad Aunt… yes maam, me wi sell off… might even catch miggle day bus maam."

"Good, yu won't sleep inna service tomorrow."

"Oh no do me so bad, the heart willin, but…"

"Me chile, the flesh is weak, He understand."

"Yu bring de little one wid yu today?"

"Him birt'day… bring him fe little air out…"

"I don't have much Youtman, buy some sweetie."

"Thanks Miss Pinnie…"

"Well missis me not going to tarry… me have to catch the miggle day bus…yu know how it go me dear…"

"Maas Willie want fe learn fe cook."

"Unless no bulla cake not over shop… me pressin oon."

"Awright den Aunt… awright little man."

"Awright Miss Pinnie… thanks for the thing." I get an approving look from Mama.

We move along, she greets almost everyone, fortunately more briefly than Miss Pinnie, with her litany of familiarity-based greetings: "Hi beloved," to Cousin Reena with her mouth is tool full with day-old soup.

To Miss Winnie and Sister D from Hilltop: "Hello Sister Dear."

And to Aunt Tidy: "Fambly wha' a bruk?"

"T'ings slow."

"Lawd me sis t'ings slow bad."

"It no too bad now but it did better dis mornin.'"
Produce is everywhere. Green and ripe bananas:
Lakatan, Gross Mitchell and Robusta along with
plantains; White and yellow heart breadfruit; Ugly fruit,
Jackfruit, white and pink grapefruit; Negro, Yellow,
S'inVincen', White and Barby yams; Chocho; Mar'
seedless, Parson Brown, Valencia and Navel oranges;
tangerines; limes; jelly and dry coconuts; Paw-paw;
cocoe; cocoa; dasheen; star and otahiti apples and ribbon
cane are relegated to the perimeter of the market. These
vendors trust their vendor neighbours implicitly as,
should the need arise to leave their stalls; it is these
folks upon whom they must depend. Vendors sitting
along the market's periphery have similar pieces of
lumber, which they use to span the gutter, with runoff
water trickling beneath their wares. Is not the first day
leaf drop into water it rotten: they use the adage's
application to stave off premature spoilage from
saturation. Vendors with delicate commodities such as
red and gungo peas, tomatoes, ginger and pimentos
and other spices, head sugar, bammie, starch, parched
and ground coffee, rope tobacco, thyme, tomato,
escallion, onion, garlic, meat, fish, and cinnamon pay
more for entry and are therefore able to place their

wares on the inside as opposed to placing them on the building's peripheral grounds, so, barring torrential conditions, they and their wares will remain dry. The islanders' perception is that when rain wet us we're going to melt or some such thing, so we go to extreme measures to remain dry; including running like the dickens to get out of a surprise shower; not to mention the fact that we students often avoid school, with the idea that teacher won't come; meetings are cancelled and even church will suffer from poor attendance because of inclement weather.

Bartering is in full swing. Predictably, the higglers start with an inflated price. These vendors are very co-operative towards each other. Of course, if a small group of them happen to have a commodity that seems scarce: "Sister D!"

"Yes Aunt Tidy"

"Yu realize a yu one in here have red peas…"

"Then fe me business chune!"

"Yu siddung pretty… yu can name yu price!"

Errand boys earn pocket money ferrying information or commodities throughout the market. They are the eyes and ears of opportunities too difficult to spot by the stationary vendors who sometimes use them to make purchases then resell at higher prices where that commodity is scarce. Because everybody has his or her favourite side to shop, this particular scheme works out rather well. When doing so, they pretend their wares are volatile or otherwise dangerous to shoppers, yelling on their way down the aisles: "Hot Water, hot water!" Or: "Watch out! Fire stick!" Or "Hot coal! Hot coal!" Shoppers lunge sideways as if responding to a siren. Once they clear the way, most shoppers turn to see the reason for their evasive manoeuvre. The sight of the merchandise may jog one's memory as to its necessity.

Sitting, the expanse of their wide skirts allow them to cascade portions between their thighs and hang some over their knees, maintaining the facade that they are all ladies. The cadre of Higglers accepts a small group of men into their club: These are the meat sellers of cows, hogs and goats.

In keeping with the adage: Waste not want not, the lower socio-economic class treats the entire kill as meat. We acquire the taste for the less expensive sections such as the brains, testicles and intestines. We culture them into delicacies. For instance the brains we scramble with eggs; the testicles we fry or roast; the cod we use in a soup we consider an aphrodisiac and, the intestines we cook with broad beans as the highlight meal of the week for many. The skins, heads, hoofs, feet and tails, after being singed and scraped, all become delicacies as well. Proles planning to eat any portion of the skin need copious amounts of water, lots of wood and time, since skins don't cook in a hurry. The sellers, like the Higglers, are also adept at mentally computing the different rates for the portions: soup bones, hindquarters, ribs, legs and so on. Their skill, with a machete, borders on the supernatural.

Most vendors wear knotted headscarves. Others wear straw hats with matching bands. The headgear protects their hair from the airborne dust and the fires' soot. Their common red, white and black plaid seems to be a display of solidarity.

Bibs on the front of their dresses provide a place to store money. Those in it for the long haul, sleeping at the same spot, when they nap, have an exposure problem as the bibs contents are tempting commodities for some low budget unemployed folks. To deny a pickpocket purloining opportunities while they sleep, other places must be used to rebuff the creeps. The purse of choice is a thread bag. The vault for this cash-stash is a pendulous place that harbours big affinity in the hearts and minds of most tropical males. Some seasoned and savvy vendors attach their Thread-bags to the straps of their braziers others simply lift, place and let gravity do the rest.

I wander away from Mama, onto the rolling slope of open space, at the rear of the market. The bareback donkeys and mules --personal taxis-- graze alongside their short-term counterparts, which remain saddled while their owners shop. Beyond the animals, in the surrounding farmlands, sits a co-ed pit toilet. Some calls of nature get substitute positions within and without the privy as some residents go further afield on the soggy ground and fertilize the banana and orange trees directly. Some even hold things longer than nature intends. Days.

Mama seems to lose her mind when she looks around and I am missing. Finding me, she grasps my arm so tightly; developing gangrene is a real possibility.

Our eastbound bus/taxi station is across the road from goddie's shop. Waiting passengers seem to be bringing everything home: Bag feed for pigs and chickens (No dog chow here, puss food? Ditto). For the chicks there's the grower for speedy weight gain, for the hens there is layer and for Sunday dinner-destined birds, fattener. The cock chickens in the group will go first as rumour has it 'their meat swell.'

It's the sideman's responsibility to safely load the carrier; he has to systematically allot spaces for different destinations; distribute the pieces to promote the lowest centre of gravity; as well as maintain the spaces under the passenger compartment; curbside and at the rear; remember and be able to identify them once their owner disembarks. Though placed in identical bags, any sideman will demonstrate his remarkable memory by matching disembarking passengers and their luggage, on the first try. He capably does this day, night, rain or shine. He deserves the Most Valuable Participant, M.V.P. award daily, because he is the only 'Yardie' that must work in the rain. Linoleum, coir mattress, bedspring, suitcase, goblet-basin-pail and chimmey set, grip, dinette set, kerosene oil stove, ironing board, broom, couple bags of cement and few sheets of zinc are loaded atop the bus and we are off by one thirty Jamaica time.

Invariably, the routes entail night travel. Now the sideman must use a bottle torch to search closely among the incendiary wrappings and markers to locate a described item. And this guy is a parochial school dropout!

The bus arrives; Canute exits to relieve himself and have the necessary couple drinks of rum, the exiting passengers disembark, we board but my favourite seat is taken so I sit at a curbside window, next to Mama. Conflicting odours permeate the bus. The body odours of passengers who have been short on deodorant from day one and are now into their third day without a bath compete with that of the single Rastaman in the back-seat who has been performing all sorts of physically demanding and stressful perspiration inducing farming activities as well as smoking his ware in the same suit of clothes for at least two weeks; compete with the self induced aromas of the exhausted market vendors' as well as those of their meals of brown stew chicken, calalloo, ackee and salt fish, fritters and johnnycakes; with smokers who light up a piece of rope tobacco. These odours, rather than blend, challenge each other for supremacy and automatically the drafted passengers become judges of this whiff-cathalon.

The thought of piloting this ground ship keeps crossing my mind. It seems everybody must drive drunk but since I'm too young to buy a drink, I buy an ice cream in the cone from a roaming vendor for six pence and coconut drops from another for penny hape'ny. I have a shilling, and four pence hape'ny left. Still under the British system with its Pound, Shilling and Pence, all with varying amounts of units, like the Higglers; I still need no calculator to figure out my change.

Canute depresses the starter button; she fires. Soon, the conductress with her flair for instant recall of faces and unique powers of recollection as to recent embarkees comes by to collect. The moment the police station is next to us, he gears down, utilizing the gearbox's ratios to apply engine braking to descend the steep grade. Although he lives on the horn, he does not apply it just willy-nilly anymore because the horn and brakes share the compressed air in the reservoir. A worst-case scenario could be that over use of the horn leaves him without brakes, unable to negotiate a corner, the consequences could be catastrophic. He conserves the air. The curbside of the bus remains in close proximity to the amputated branches of established evergreen trees such as Guango, Poinciana, Willow, Lignum vitae (our national tree), Bastard Cedar, Cedar and Mahoe in one area and citrus trees in others. Those by the side of the road are in a state of constant pruning; thanks to the way the drivers of large vehicles hug their corners. The road narrows, and amputated branches move much closer to my window than I care to see. He pilots the bus in such a way that dismembered branches overhanging the road are kept a breath away from the curbside mirror and less than an inch from the rearmost windows. Motivating downhill at a faster clip -twenty-eight miles per hour- the world is simply rushing by. To requisition a stop, one must anticipate the stopping distance of a vehicle they've never driven and then tug on this string that causes pealing like a mini church bell rings so that they may alight. Soon, it's a blur of embarking and disembarking. His stops still fail to give away any secrets with reference to signs-of-life and the alighting passengers do so without requesting alternate points. Unlike some drivers that stop at many bars to have a drink, he stops at very few as it seems he's got someone special or 'something on ice' further down the road or at the terminus.

Bredda Man dispatches him again: "Go-so-bus."

The added speed with which he negotiates the turns highlights the side-to-side motion of the bus' body. Motion sickness is taking its toll on me the unseasoned traveller. I'm uncomfortably hot. Perspiration is washing me like sweat. I tell Mama I don't feel good and she instinctively knows what it is. She opens her purse and removes folded sheets of newspaper, expands two of them to a size approximately the width of my chest, places them under my shirt and keeps a few in her hand, obviously some form of remedy. I hope she's right but even as she is pulling my head close to her breast, patting the exposed side with her palm... I still feel unsure as the taste of the sardines and pepper float on the copious amounts of saliva my glands have started producing to the taste buds on my tongue. She comforts me: "Yu wi soon feel better Sonny. My request for comforting comes too late. As my body convulses and gets ready to heave it all, she cups additional sheets of newspaper below my mouth. I do a good job of hitting the target and she does an exquisite job of making it deep enough to prevent any backwashes. My sardines are gone, so too the pepper and my cream soda, ice cream and drops. Coupled with the digestive juices, the mix does not smell too good. Mama folds it up and wipes the remnants of perspiration from my face. She removes the newspaper sheets from my chest, carefully wraps them together and secures the clasped bundle on the floor between her feet. At the next stop she pokes her head through the window and asks Bredda Man to dispose of the package. I doze off. Soon I am awakened as we are near home. The gastric expulsion process plus the rest helps me to quickly return to my old self, and I cannot wait to tell my friends about the bus ride above everything else that occurred.

Mama summons Rev to catch fresh curry chicken in the making. Using a handful of dry corn to round up the rooster and fowls, he allows Mama to point out today's candidate for the festivities. She issues commands,

"Jasmine!"

"Yes Aunt!"

"Grater one coconut and some sweet potato."

"Yes'n. A pitayta pone you a make maam?"

"Is me grandson birthday you know pickney!"

"Me membah Maam."

"Dellie oh!"

"Yes Mama."

"Break one coconut and cut it up."

"Yes maam."

"Dahlia! Boil some water fe pluck the chicken."

"Yes Aunt."

"Rev, yu kill, pluck and cut him up fe me."

"Yes Mama, but is a hen you point out mam!"

"You know what me mean."

"Yes maam."

"Me wi cook mi grandson chicken me self."

The riddle asks, "What has hell atop, hell a' bottom and hallelujah in the middle?" The answer to which is.... Pudding. Having few ovens the national baking method is to place the mixture, in this case grated sweet potatoes; a little flour; a little cornmeal; a dash of: nutmeg, vanilla, rose water; the grated coconut's squeezed juice and a handful or two of the grated shards atop the mixture with a little butter mixed in; the blackened aluminium container --pudding pan-- atop a wood burning fireplace and then placing some of the lit firewood atop the cover of the mix and keeping it under a controlled burn for about an hour and a half. I love the way she takes and sprinkles some of the grated coconut atop of the mix; this way when it's baked the top is of a much thinner consistency, like hot but set jello more so than the cornmeal and potato mix below. Dellie breaks the coconut and through its initial fracture shares the trickling water, by direct consumption, with Jasmine before breaking it out of the husk.

Once caught, Rev tucks the bird's head under one of its wings, locates a small bucket and, seizing his machete along the way, heads for the exposed guinepp tree root. Keeping its body under the pan and with one swing of the 'las' he beheads the bird. He lifts the bucket and releases the body, an act which validates the statement, "…and running like a chicken with its head cut off," the body, in a zig zag motion covers the same ground twice. Out of breath and blood it lays down for the last time.

Mama makes the beverage. I love brown sugar and lime brebbage, which will go with the pone (pudding) for dessert. To make the brebbage wicked gone to bed, Mama, on special occasions, buys a thrupance block of ice from Nowee the one-arm ice and ice cream vendor I daydream about in church, so we can enjoy little coolings.

Rev ribs me, "A spoil you spoil…"

Dahlia adds, "Is because you a dem grandson."

I'm being pestered, pinched, poked, pushed and prodded by Rev, Jasmine, Dahlia and Yvonne as a result of my good fortune. Telling Mama and Dada about their abusive behaviour draws their wrath but makes it worse for me in the long run as the abusive recourse from each of them is sure. But I cry and run to tell them anyway.

While we have dinner, the sweet potato pudding simmers. By the time evening bus arrives, the pudding is cool enough to be had and we all have a slice. When some market people, some of the same friends Mama visited with earlier in the day stop by, Mama gi' dem wan lickle twep to taste.

Dusk approaches and that's our clue to congregate and tell duppy stories. Ackee Red blurts out, "Well me a go river go wash me foot before it dark up."

"Me to!" Canepiece Rat announces. We tiptoe back. Having no slippers to put on, only compulsory activities like getting more food and adult commanded errands are carried out. We join the duppy stories session in progress in the western-enterance blocking corner of the shop. Some congregants live a far way off, the lighting system at their home is so poor, and sleep takes so long to come and the boredom seems so eternal that it's more productive to congregate and share stories and in the African way of living have some things passed down strictly by word of mouth.

Some adopted teens, friends and family like Sheppie, Mongoose, Bear, Bull, Annancy and Duck Foot stop by and join in the pre-bedtime jokes and storytelling. I tip toe away from the group for a moment with the explanation that I'm going to beg Mama another slice of the pudding, which she freely gives me. As I return to the group, they fall eerily silent except for Mongoose. He suggests, "No bite no more!"

"Why not."

"Because a have something new to teach you."

"Bout what?"

"How to digest food!"

"What dat!"

"Take food from me belly into yours man."

"A true! How dat!"

"Jus press yu big toe gainst mine when me eat!"

"Really?"

I can't articulate it, but this has to be Osmosis.

"You think me a joke!"

He has my attention: "No! Me never say so."

"Gi'e me you pone n put you toe gainst mine."

I hesitate.

"Yu no chuss me?"

"…Yea… but…"

"Whe yu tink me a go do… run way?"

"No… but…"

"Gi'e me de sinting!"

"… Awright… See it here."

"Put you big toe, toe to toe with my own."

"Which one?"

"It no matter."

"Like so?"

"How them say you fool?" He takes a bite. "Allright me a go chew now. When me swallow you will feel it…. You feel it?"

I'm swayed, "Yes."

Taking another bite and enjoying the particles his molars masticate and he demonstrates genuine concern each time my knitted brows make me seem doubtful. Not wanting to seem unable to extract food from one's body into mine through one's big toe, I soon feel the transfer after each bite till it is all gone.

Under the cloak of darkness, Mama takes her leave from the non-stop banter and uses copious amounts of water to take her bath on the barbeque in the love-seat sized, two-foot deep, oval, oscillating-bottom bath pan. Not known, is the fatality count on the symbiotic mosquito larvae succumbing with the scum from the soap.

There is no problem in getting us to bed as the day's activities invariably leave us worn out. The lamps

upstairs in the bedrooms have long since been lit, along with the bed-glasses placed in their respective rooms. Me tip toe upstairs, change me clothes, pee pee in the bed glass and say me "Genkle Jeezas... Bless Mama, bless Dada, bless everybody. Amen.
Goodnight Mama. Dada goodnight. Rev goodnight. Jasmine, Dahlia, Yvonne goodnight. Goodnight Dellie." I am beneath the sheet before all my goodnights are returned.

Chapter Ten

I AM UNAWARE OF THE ROOSTER'S cacophony once again but as I awake knowing it's church day and be it during Sunday school, or service the feat of getting onto the pew awaits. But I can do it myself. Rib by rib I pull myself up onto the pew then wiggle into place. I sit there; swing my feet and miss most of the stuff parson postulates, until after eleven o'clock bus passes. Pre-selecting a pew with a view of the road, curious attendees crane their necks to pry into disembarking passengers' comings and goings. Mama is not a member of the bus-curious club so our dedicated seat is the first pew in the rear quadrant on the far side. Positioned next to the door. It affords easy bathroom access, with the least disruption.

The passing bus driver respectfully refrains from using the klaxon except in the face of imminent danger. The female-centric-spiritualists long-since, before "Whappy kill Phillop" cease testifying with a view to winning the souls of their un-repentant significant other's for The Lord.

The way: -
She
Sis Ethel
Sister 'B'
Sister 'D'
Sister 'G'
Sister 'I'
Sister 'S'
Sister Sweetie
Sister 'V'
Aunt Essie
Aunt Assie
Aunt Ettie
Aunt Freda
Aunt Gertie
Aunt Letty
'T'Ida

'T'Mary

Mama Florie

Ma' Mary

Miss Winnie

stay Heaven-bound sharp is; by frequently testifying among themselves as The Spirit leads: "Every time Hi feel action that could cause a contradiction with The Spirit moving in my heart I pray for less contention ...yes my bradders and sisters, glad ham Hi to stand in your midst today and to be able to mention wonderful and glorious things that he The Lord of Creation has done for me... standing in your midst today, word cannot express all of the wonderful t'ings that The Lord has done for me. When Hi first met My Fahder I was bored I had nothing left for me to discover in the whole world having been from Border to Bull Savanna seen sight untold there is no one this world cannot offer or give silver or gold that can any longer keep me from De Precious Lord's fold The Saviah Jeezas pull me from that so terrible awful road to oblivion without doubt I was spiralling uncontrolled down the path to destruction doing all that was wrong Involve myself in every wrong kind of sin a can't mention. Hin-this-world-of-sinners-pray-for-me-while-Hi-continue-to-pray-for-you-in-Jesus-name amen. Alleluia Glory to

Gaat oh ray toe taw. Askalla boo I know you. Oh glory, oh rae tow taw, glory!"

Pastors of the flock have two occasions to cast the spiritual net at the sea of sinners: funerals and weddings. The few men who run the gauntlet and develop spiritual mettle have it constantly tested in and out of the sanctuary.

*   *   *

Conquistadors roaming beyond district perimeters risk participating in blood shedding skirmishes. Such a man must be prepared to go to war for what he wants, if what he wants is worth warring for. Transportation: automobile; horse; mule or jackass, is assumed to be the man's responsibility. An operator is assumed to be the owner. Assumption awards him automatic respect and free reign within his trusty steed's capably covered terrain. A testosterone driven car in a new town is assurance to his acquisitions.

White Man, the descendant with the miscegenation conjuring sobriquet lives in a feeder district of our bushtropolis. He is Busha's overseer for two coffee farms. He resides on the larger: Coffee Piece. The other is in Morant. Men being men, damsels being damsels, Prudence from Morant, does a simul-tickle on two hearts and that's how the altercation begins.

Euclid's a man with teeth as white and skin as dark as God allows has a physique bestowed only on those who till soil and toil from sunrise to sunset. His musculature impresses the fairer sex. He engages Prudence in more than conversations, satiated; he suffers a memory lapse and denies her new addiction.

Colour goes a far way on The Rock but being deficient in its producer, melanin, goes even further. White Man spots the seemingly unattached damsel and the lyrics of his conversation falls on attentive ears. Euphoric Prudence accepts more than conversation. Colonialism bestows more options and opportunities on those who look more like White Man. A concept on the future dances in her head: ...an offspring, opening of double doors, personal office, boardroom meetings, walks on hardwood floors she can only clean.

The axiom proves true: What is done in the dark soon comes to light. Prudence's tête-à-tête evades sidetracked Euclid. She's keenly aware of the expected child's genetics, but remains quiet. Euclid, on seeing the offspring, realises he's in a real ring ding; that in fact she had the fling with the local man that resembles the king. He schedules a meeting to squelch their loathing. Bright and early Saturday morning White Man appears in the town square; all children's play cease.

The glint of his machete is blinding. Nine o'clock, sharp. There could be a killing.

His adrenaline pumping, he proceeds east towards Euclid's home. Vengeance. They meet in the street, and with a practiced flair, have an expletives-smattered exchange and transform in to combatants. Half mile away the sound of machetes meeting with bad intentions demonstrates their seriousness for ten minutes. Milk truck's driver interrupts their need to kill by sounding his horn; forlorn Euclid falls to the roadway. His profusely bleeding body is tossed aboard the truck.

From our second story veranda I see Euclid, prostrate, flash by: the fallen, crestfallen, the lesser man. Momentarily, White Man can be heard shouting wildly, he bleeds from a single wound to his right hand. It needs no stitches. He repeats himself to the awe-struck citizenry: "When a go down there an im come out, im chap after me fus, and me just cotch it like so," he says with his palm held high and Maybell his machete in his left. Continuing with a devilish grin, "An a chop im pon im right shoulder," He pauses for effect, "An im stagger way an a jus call back pon Maybell." He rips a sleeve from his shirt, grips it between his teeth, tears it lengthwise, bandages his hand with one half, and uses the other as an upper-arm tourniquet then proceeds home. Euclid is hospitalized for two weeks. Them say if he had arrived two minutes later, he would have died.

*   *   *

Third Sunday is Baba's time. In true secular style we remember and pray for the sick and shut in collection-throwing members of this church. Stah Duncie reads the bulletins and we are brought to a state of readiness to hear the day's word. I wiggle off the pew to sing the offertory hymn from Mama's Hymnal. We share the Bible also because The New Testament I got for my birthday is impractical whenever Baba hits the rostrum. But whatever scripture or Sanky he references, Mama locates and places under my nose. Sheet music is way beyond me so Mama points to the lines and I try to read around her knuckle.

Baba Laiza gets things going as God, without fail, sends His lengthiest messages through him. When it comes to pulpit stamina, no matter how holy and gifted any man of the cloth from near or far thinks he is; him can't touch Baba. And though he's illiterate, his sermons arrive verbatim: Book, chapter and verse. He rifles through The Good Book by air. His timely thought processes elicit stimulated, simulated donkey braying while his verbosity allows him to fill space with inappropriate, mispronounced, polysyllabic words. Few in the audience can challenge him on their meanings and those that can have insular jobs they like and are simply doing the ritualistic thing.

Once the sermon begins, I can drift with my thoughts while he bellows at his best. He frequently repeats himself so half of anyone's attention assures the attendee receives a full message. I pass much of this spiritually serenading time anticipating ice cream Mama will purchase from One-hand Nowee after service. I'm unaware that sugar is an ingredient in cones and feel strongly that his armpit's grip, sans napkin, is a significant contributor to its sweet taste. My inattention is lost in a sea of glazed, half-sleepy, bone-weary, tired-eyed souls. Active participants needn't voice comments, as Baptist Church members aren't big on, nor are expected to have, Pochomania-styled outbursts.

We are all God's children... but. Our visiting members are to be credited with the volleys of competitive outbursts which encourage the mob mentality and cause two of our normal 'Amen' sisters, Gramma and Stah Duncie, in the spirit of competition, to shout: "Oh Glory, Yes Jeezas and Tenk you Gaad." Gramma gets outdone, two to one.

Having visitors on Baba's Sundays is the worst thing that can happen, because the last thing he needs is a little spurring on. Some people sleep and wake and I even run out of daydreams while he continues to bray data-streams. Mama does not share my sentiments. She wants me to soak this stuff up like a sponge and retain it more than the close-minded stuff teacher teaches over school.

On one hand, If I absorb this thing, have perfect attendance at Sunday School, memorize every Golden Text, participate in the meeting house dynamics of Gatha and Blanche, take the Godeology thing to the max and fail everything over school, I might as well go bruk stone a roadside as there is no bonafide-capitalist job that will pay me zilch. I'll end up an eighty-year-old, barefoot grandfather who lacks the respect of my own offspring. Should I grow up and in my working for Buckra barefoot state, give my mistress the pay cheque to dent the ongoing required bill over Ackee Red's shop, and then carry the rest to parson?

On the other hand, if I wallow in all the academics they'll permit, outstanding things can result. I could, become a civil servant. Funny! Crack the academic success code and you large. Everybody either knows you or dying to meet you. The bigger your car, house, bank account and plantation, the more people know you. Notoriety gets you relatives, island wide. End up a nobody and blood relatives disown you. Figure it out, get big and donate a Church Organ, a new wing, bell and tower, set of steps and you are thought of, in the same nerve impulse, through the neuron's axon, as The Big Guy Himself.

Walking the mile home, we drift into a group trailing the adults and playing whatever games we can get away with. Keeping in mind that it's Sunday, we can't get too rambunctious or we'll be whipped for messing up our Sunday best. We spot a parked car. Mama gleefully says to no one in particular, "A bet a da bway ya Pupa."
Ackee Red's mother replies, "Yu expec' him Aunt?"

"Him generally come fe de bway birthday."

"Put two an' two together so yu prably right…"
Beyond our neighbours' Aralias, we see two figures conversing on the piazza; Mama's pace quickens. Others try staying with her but Sister D and Gramma and Aunt Tidy maintain their pace. Gang Gang Galina, who is bringing up the rear, "Hehem, we have too far fe go fe go keep up wid dem sprucy one dem whe t'ink the surprise a go run way." Mama replies, "A no so, him probably a visit long time."

"Hunnu can gallang leave me bra."

"Me too Sistah," says Sistah D. The gap widens. Mama says: "Hunnu tek time walk good," she adds, "Me can mek him out, Gad go wid hunnu."

Sistah D: "Yu to Aunt, tell him howdy fe me."
Aunt Tidy, "Beg yu gi him a hearty howdy fe me too."

From his imposing five feet five, he stoops in front of me; with a meticulous moustache and a radiant smile he asks, "So how are you doing in school my son?" His voice almost rumbles like thunder. "Good sah." I develop a sudden interest in the piazza of that 1919 construction which has started to show its age. Directing his attention to Mama he asks, "So how are you my second mother?"

"Son, thenk God fe Jeezas me still holdin' on."

"Holdin on! You not goin nowhere now Mama."

"Is more than one time you tell me that son."
Dada chimes in, "Den Iris come fix sup'm fe eat no!" Silence hangs, Mama would like to say, Lawd wait nuh Willie, a person don't even put down them bag and Bible yet. If you think him hungry you couldn't have one of them gal fix sup'm. Me nuh even find out how Mummah and Bud-Joe do! Lawd Willie. But wives here don't disrespek their husbands like that.

"Mama, come off you feet my dear, I'm alright. I had bun and cheese and drink an aerated water." Mama smiles, thinking: See Willie... him naw drop dung. She voices: "Yu naw less than yu bun an cheese eh?"
Eyes roving, he says to Mama, "So how the service."

Terrence R. E. Burey

"Baba preach, God seems to always give him more to deliver...."

"Oh, that's why you are late!"

"That plus yu son and him ice cream."

Passing stragglers interrupt their conversation to say hello. "Cho, Good Gad Iris, we can talk 'round the table."

Changed from their Sunday best, my friends return to inspect the car. I won't have to change right away because he always takes pictures of me. I brag, "See how me father car boasty though!" They ignore my comment.

Trailing on the wind I hear Dada, "Then come we go inside no! Me already open the front staircase..."

Mama disdains it because of her claustrophobia, "Well Willie you know me walkin' 'round the back."

"Then I will just come with you Miss I."

My smile growing, Ackee Red airs his jealousy, "Him boasy eh, watch him face." Then he rediricts with a direct, "So yu tink a fe u pupa one gat cyar."

"Me never say that but smaddy mus jealous."

"A who yu a call jaalas?" Chest-to-chest.

"A you, you a come tell me bout me boasy!"

Canepiece-Rat interrupts us, "Although cockroach no business in a fowl fight...." He says, "The two of hunnu behave man, people not suppose to fight 'pon Sunday."

184

"Nuh Ackee Red come jump up inna me face, me no know a wha fly inna him head?"

"Him too braggadocios and boasy ma, a show off... like say a fe him pupa one can drive car!"
Me: "Fe yu can drive? ... It must be fowl offa nest, ha! ha!"
Momentarily overcome by the humour, Ackee Red joins in the laughter: "Ah bwoy, people a tek bad tings make joke."
Canepiece Rat needles: "Yu tek tings too serious man!"

"But him no fe talk 'bout me father man! Him no have nothin' fe do with this!" He quickly adds: "Plus Papa going buy him own goods truck one day."
Me: "Mout mek fe say anything, dat nuh mean one biscuit."
Ackee Red challenges, "Yu calling me fader a liar bway?"

"Me throw me corn, me no call no fowl!"

"But a mus' me fader yu talkin' bout."

"Yu pick it up a'ready and it down yu belly."

"Bak a dog a dawg, but befor' dog a mista dog."
Making a fist with his thumb sandwiched between his index and middle fingers he throws the sandwiched finger in my face, rotates his stiff arm in a clockwise and counter clockwise motion, and says, "Yu better smell yu daddy gunpowder."

"A wha' di back foot! If a nay one t'ing y'see, cho." Feeling victorious in the exchange I retreat.

From overhead on the veranda, "What hunnu doing?"

In unison, "Nothin.'"

We all laugh it off.

"Son I'm coming down to take some pictures."

"Boy, come here first let me look at you."

"Comin' Mama. Meeysuehunnu."

Running an index finger the length of his car, I head upstairs through the claustrophobic, to Mama but gargantuan to me, front stairwell, push up the trapdoor, and present for inspection. Mama calls: "Sonny! Come look at your presents!"

"Coming Maam!"

"You see what you father bring for you?"

"No Mama me just coming from downstairs."

"Well see them here!"

"Yes Mama."

"You know is what?"

"No Maam."

"Well make we see together no!"

"Yes Maam."

"Me just as excited as you you know!"

"A true Mama!"

She replies: "Well see them here; dungaree trousers, drip dry shirt and comic book."

"Them pretty Mama."

'Drip dry,' a new phenomenon. Reading the label and grasping the wash and wear concept, I'm anxious for the clothes to get dirty, to see how illiterate Mamus the washa humman, will wash it on my body using either a dried cornstick or the clapper and scrubbing board used to literally beat the colour out of the fabric without taking my life.

"You can read what the book say Sonny?"

"Some of it Mama!"

"What the name on the cover say?"

"Same thing what you just see on it Mama!"

"But wait! You taking liberty with me boy!"

"No Mama."

Mama beckons: "Come in the room with me sonny." She damps a rag, dabs a little soap on it and removes a layer of skin from my face, to get rid of the sheen that's a part of our make-up, then tries to do the same to my arms and legs: You did bathe this morning?

"Yes Mama." Her push on my shoulder creates a full anatomical wobble, "Stannup, stannup, what's the matter wid you?"

"Nutten Mama."

"Then whey you no' stan tuddy?" I think: If you trying to push me through the wall what do you expect? But prudently voice: "Nutten Mama."

187

I get a full application of oil. It quickly replenishes all the lost sheen, on my forehead and nose. My sticks for legs, with humongous knots in the bramble at the knees run a strong second. I lose newly-formed epi and endodermis to the hairbrush again. We roll, portfolio prepped and she presents me with the announcement: "Him ready!"

"Thank you Mama. Him look good as gold."

By the church of God, just out of earshot of my jealous, jeering cronies with a backdrop of hibiscus -- shoeblack because it is actually rubbed on one's black shoes to deepen the lustre-- he has me face the sun. With the sun's rays directly into my eyes, he commands: "Hold that flower and look into the camera." I now have a compound problem: stepping beyond my level of comprehension in a new vernacular and looking in the direction of sound which the sun obstructs from view with its retina piercing rays.

"The wha sah!"

"Oh this! Let me explain…" A novel idea.

"Yes sah."

"My camera! I want to record images of you, so that when you become a man I can you and I and anyone else for that matter can take a look at them and see what you looked like when you were a boy. So I want to take your photograph!"

"Oh sah."
I pose
for another series of pictures.
Dad relishes the opportunity
to turn skin and bones into fine art.
As his subject I must play the part.

Kneel here,
look there,
and tilt your head this way,
now that,
not that,
like this, stand here, spin around,
face the sun, smile now, and don't squint.

He reloads.
I learn another thousand ways
to hold a leaf
while it's still connected to the tree.
Then I learn of a hundred thousand ways
to admire a hibiscus flower!
A million and one positions
in which to sit,
smile,
stand, stare, squat, stoop,
stop blinking,

stay blinking still,
split the blinking petals,
swoon over the blooming gift,
seem blooming satisfied with self;
suck breeze, say cheese, stifle sneeze
and scratch grass itches on my arms
and jeans bruises on my knees.

"Look at the camera. Say cheese. That's a boy."
Its manual features combined with his distrust of anyone
operating his prized possession preclude his taking a
picture with me. He has me posing in repose; holding
this croton, that hibiscus and the other blade of grass;
then I change into my new long pants for more pictures.
He takes shots of Mama and myself, Dada declines:
"P'Cho, no sah." Then demurely adds, "Yu gallang
Iris. Yu take good pickcha, plus yu have on clothes
a'ready."

Chapter Eleven

BACK HOME, THE BEST GLASSES VACATE
spots they hold on the doilies in the cabinet. Jasmine
announces: "Hunnu please to come fe dinner."
Mama quickly chides her: "Do we have a dinner bell?"
She answers with a trailing bit of sarcasm: "Yeeeees
Aunt."

"Whey it mek for?"

"Fe ring Aunt."

On weekdays we eat downstairs behind the tailor shop
but today, as with other special occasions, we gather in

the upstairs dining room where the linen tablecloth is always spread but seldom used.

"Sonny, say you grace mek you father hear!"

"Yes Dada."

The adults chew food and chew the fat. We are seen and not heard. We speak when spoken to and answer when told.

Dada: "Dahlia oh."

"Yes Dada!"

"Yu fegat sup'm."

"Wha Dada? Oh la la, sorry Dada. And me wash the pepper and everything you know Dada! Excuse…"

I refuse sour sop juice in favor of anticipated aerated water from dad. Done eating, the adults go to the front verandah with toothpicks --three sticks of Dada's matches without the sulphur-- to deliberate. I'm back to my friends, back so thick that one would wonder if is we same one had a disagreement before. Before long my Dad interrupts our play, stooping to get to my height he rumbles, "I'm leaving now son… would you like anything?"

"Yes sah!"

"Yes Daddy." In a familiar maternal voice.

"Yes Daddy."

"What would you like mi son?"

"One soda sah, one soda daddy!"

"How about two?"

"Two sah!" My eyes go skyward to the veranda, we make eye contact, "Two Daddy!"

He nods, "Very well," he hands me a two and sixpence piece. I see a shiny ring, bigger than Mama's on the ring finger of his right hand, he says, "Buy your sodas and keep the change to buy a book and pencil and anything else, but buy the book first. O.K.!"

Mama clears her throat. I hear her: "Thank you daddy!"

He rubs the crown of my head: "I'll post the pictures."

Mama: "I know me son, drive good."

Ackee Red and Canepiece Rat beg for some of my aerated waters, I give the standard response: "Who beg naw get and who no beg no want." We share the second bottle.

Shortly after Dahlia lights the lamps, it's "Gentle Jesus..." time and that's my last conscious moment of February 15, 1960.

I am still mastering the art of dreams and subconscious bladder control. Things stay dry providing it's not coconut, cane, orange, guava, mango, plum, star apple, tamarind, guinepp or otahiti apple time, no late brebbage, no cocoa tea, bush tea and crackers, two aerated water birthdays. Or the big boys go torching for fish in the river, come back and we stay up late and run boat –cooking everything together in a kerosene tin with white rice and with the shrimps, African Perch, Eel, Majjo and Crayfish them chop as the fish lay sleeping in the open.

Older heads also say it helps if I don't play with fire before retiring. Apparently, it causes one to think one is a dousing fireman…. I will have this pee pee bed issue under control as soon as I can make the subconscious distinction between my recurring dreams and reality.

Tonight is one such night. In the dream I'm in bed with the need to pee. I rise but neglect to use the chimmey under my single bed and instead walk into Mama's room to use her pail. The ambient lighting in her room reveals even the details in the mural on the bed glass. The violet trim rings fade into the white geraniums. I watch the stream, a sidewinder; as it meanders down the slope of the lid and disappear under the raised centre handle. Oooh, relief. Gradually, I'm aware of wonderful warmth. Wonderful, pleasurable, warmth, spreading from just below my waist…. And because I sleep on my stomach it heads north to my chest and south towards my knees. Oh what a feelin'… Time freezes as the realization hits. But because my bladder muscles have not been instructed to alter their state, there is no ebb in the flow. Suddenly conscious, my entire body springs off the bed. Gravity takes over and I hit the floor, knees first, head last.

Both Mama and Dada snore so they drown the sound. When a warm liquid hits the warm tropical air, its temperature along with that of its contact patch, drops due to evaporation. I'm freezing, tryin' to figure out how the 'H' 'E' two sticks --hell-- this could happen to me again…. The flow interrupted, I save the remainder for my chimmey.

My coir mattress is a penetrable fibrous product of coconut husks. It physical characteristics disallows copious water retention, so streaming through the mattress, the urine puddles under the bed then heads for the space between the floorboards to the ground floor's concrete slab, just in front of Mama's three-burner kerosene stove. I'm mad at myself for doing this again: Forgetting again to try one last time before going to bed.

Without waking Mama, I quietly find pyjamas and a sheet in the lower bureau drawers. In the best of times it is hard to open. This is not the best of times. If I can just make daylight for my fingers though…. I'm in. I'm good.

Changed, I solve the problem. I throw a dry sheet at it. I tiptoe to get some old newspapers, not yet recycled into toilet paper, wrapping paper, lamp-shade cleaner, bottle torch wick, kites, rain hat or pack-aging material, in the near corner of the great-room and place them under the bed to stem the tide. Massy me pupa, de bed middle col'. Placing most of the cover sheet under my abdomen and thighs, I try steering clear of the centre of my bed. Sleep due to hypother-mia comes quickly. I greet it worrying about Mama finding out the mattress is wet again.

Consciousness and dawn bring a pungent re-minder. However the large number of scents vying for attention sweeps my hours-old problem under the pro-verbial rug. The leftover beef and gravy in the duchy, along with the piece of potato pudding vie through the broken glass in the lower section of the cabinet. The bananas ripening downstairs in banana thrash next to Dada's charcoal for the self-heater iron in the storage room have quite a presence. The toothpaste and Car-bolic soap by the goblet and basin in Mama's room join in. The gardenia, kerosene oil, chicken coop with its foul fowl droppings, hair oil, stale urine in the pail, hog pen stench, de ram goat nex' door, boiled hog feed, and bagged pigs feed waft through the air, all fighting for recognition, but I don't know this.

Shamefully, I pull myself out of bed, dress and sneak my milk bottle off the table downstairs and try to vanish trailing what I'm sure is a very strong urine odour. I tell Mama good morning in the general vicinity of the oil stove where she declines comment, while she's almost standing in the puddle evidence. I begin the milk run; I berate myself so much, that in two twos I'm there. Manners maketh even the pee pee bed man so I meet, greet and split in low spirit, "Pee pee bed," across my forehead. Back home I go across the road and take my exposed bath. The geography offers its benefits; it's impossible to run into any kind of difficulties, as the water on this side is barely calf deep. Mama and Dada can just yell if I overstay. Shamefully I have my cocoa tea, fried plantain and mongoose bread bump breakfast, shake out my mouth with some water and without making eye contact with Mama or Dada, I bid them goodbye and leave for school. I feel like a convict in khaki. I walk over to Ackee Red's shop feeling guilty as sin; we both sound Canepiece-Rat who comes skipping across the river stones at the fording. With reading and exercise books in hand, we join the moving mass of students heading for big school.

* * *

In the junior school, girls comprise the majority of the student body. Regardless of financial constraints; whether they own a single school uniform or many;

they take pride in their uniforms. It's an art in itself, watching them take a seat in a classroom, their fingers' orchestration lays the fabric in perfect form to greet their derrieres and chairs. For the few who persevere and succeed, parents have short patience for those crediting genes, brains, anything or anyone else except Massa Gad himself.

*   *   *

They focus on keeping our young men down, ensuring that only their boys become articulate, matriculate in the prerequisites at the right schools in the right jargon with the right idiosyncrasies, ensure that the circle remains nepotistically tight. Unbroken.

By and by though, others begin to learn. Plebs begin having sons who finish parochial schools without quitting to help in the fields. The lips with scholarship information that can soften financial blows are pursed tight. We matriculate with the help of the same community that it takes to raise a child. A loan here a loan there. We start going to secondary schools. On to universities. We graduate with degrees. The sons of men farming other people's lands from sunrise to sunset begin having sons who read and comprehend books beyond rote and recitation level, begin having sons who make societal inroads.

Last month I started attending 'big school.' The rightful age of acceptance follows one's seventh birthday but my past teachers at kindergarten and infant school intimated to Mama that per the system, they believe I have some special aptitude. Things seem normal to me; I'm still interjecting before teacher finishes asking a question and giving her the right answer.

By consistently giving her the answer they say I'm bright. Bright in this case is good. Do the same thing at home, answering quickly to Mama's rhetorical questions, and she too says I'm bright. Bright here is a horse of a different colour. Bright in this case is bad. Answer quickly, if she calls you bright and yu name is Bright and yu right. Perplexing! It's the system.

'Flashing' ones' fingers in a classroom environment creates that sound teachers identify with intelligence. Throughout this early matriculation staff members do become cognizant of the fact that, *oui,* we, too are capable of surpassing any level of comprehension and analytic reasoning that our blue-blooded counterparts are bred and spoon-fed to attain. It is apparent that, as the saying goes, "All we ever needed was the chance...." My retarded growth and premature entrance to big school force me to sit up front. I gain an advantage as a result of this manoeuvre. My hand is always up in teacher's face so she recognizes my abilities. Church and state mix freely here. There are no problems with the "Our Father" prayer we say in the mornings.

Unlike everything else we learn in school, prayers are not in any book. It's the system. When we gather to say end-of-day prayers, we do so in the quadrangle and the deep bass rumble of the big boys sound just like a rolling calf. We learn by osmosis:

Lighten our darkness we beseech Thee Oh Lord
And by Thy Great Mercy
Defend us... perils and dangers of this night
By the power of Thy Only Son
Our Saviour Jesus Christ.
Amen.

In 'A' class head teecha wife does the teaching. "Forehead," the smartest of the girls and I compete neck and neck scoring first and second on all our class assignments except one; Drama, in which I clearly beat her. The ever-present but unspoken colour thing allows "Redeyboh," my brightest red skin female classmate, to play the lead role in my acting debut. We profile as star and starette in a nursery rhyme. Were the role for the leading man more upful, Ackee Red would have my lines. But I play Bere Annancy, a blacklisted spider. I'm almost up for a Grammy before leaving my granny. Forehead and I skip 'B' class at the beginning of my second year making me two years younger than most of my classmates; Forehead and I are still neck and neck here in 'C' class.

During recesses and lunchtimes, daredevil boys hang out like circus performers, dangling by their arms and legs from the rafter supports of the Cafeteria piazza's corrugated zinc overhang. Staff members are vigilant against the practice since Maahga fell and broke his hand. The fact that he is rushed to the clinic in the headmaster's car garners him a new name, 'Head-teecha-pickney.'

Everything she teaches us we get tested on, and that I suppose is fair. But should I really get graded on nursery rhymes in order to advance to a higher level of learning.

Teacher: "Good morning class!"

Students: "Mawnin teecha!"

Following the syllabus: "I hope you have learned the nursery rhyme because there are ten more to learn before you go on holiday."

Students: "Yes Teecha!"

Enthusiastically the mis-educator continues: "We will say Jack and Jill on three. And one and two…"

We do well so we learn another and the mis-education continues: "Begin Humpty Dumpty on three. And one and two…"

> Humpty Dumpty sat on a wall
> Humpty Dumpty had a great fall
> All the King's horses and all the King's men
> Couldn't put Humpty together again

We get done and Waxx the philosopher boy with the beauty spot on his forehead raises his hand and intuitively waits until he is recognized before speaking: "Teecha! I have a question Teecha!"

Teacher: "Don't I tell you to just raise your hand and not talk until you have my permission? Stand up."

Embarrassed in front of the class, he wants to demur because he knows this and has waited and knows that it's futile to go down that road with her, he is somewhat angered at the situation but is also incapable of controlling his burning desire to learn, a desire that is stronger than their desire to make us quit.

He stands: "Teecha! The part that says, '...all the King's orses and all the King's men couldn't put Uumpty together again...' is true Teecha?"

Teacher is forced to think beyond the class preparation she must do under poor conditions for less money per year than the average politician salts away in one of his offshore bank accounts in a month: "First of hall why don't you hemphasize yu hayches hare you hignorant?"

"Nooo miss." "Didn't you read it in the book?"

"Yes Teecha."

"What you have in you head! Water?"

"No Teecha."

"A novel idea. They put it in the book, but you..."

"Me what miss?"

"You coco head bwoy doubt the book?"

"A never say that miss."

"So what you questioning me for?"

"Well Teecha, orse ave oof and the guard them wear gloves in the picture right Teecha!"

"Yes. So what is your point?"

"How them scrape hegg red and patch hegg shell Teecha?"

And while she is obviously confounded by the question, he finishes what we had been discussing since receiving the assignment: "And you mean to say them even train orse to use him oof and put hegg red inside the yolk or a joke? And glue eggshell? Oorse can do jig-saw puzzle Teecha?"

Pandemonium.

She controls the situation: "I'll tell you is this! If you want to continue advancing through the classes and graduate and become a productive farmer, a contributing member of this society, you best learn all the other nursery rhymes the way you learn this one..."

"Yes Teecha." Raising a chiding finger she goes on: "Don't interrupt me! I'm not done...and save the

Terrence R. E. Burey

little space you have in your cocoa brain for what is in your reading book… don't fill it up with nonsense!"

"Yes Teecha."

"Sit down! Any more questions?" She asks, her eyes scanning the classroom.

In unison: "No Teecha!"

Ackee Red whispers under his breath: "Think bout it, 'The cow jump over the moon!' The cow them a England a must high jump champion!"

Duck Foot is in quiet stitches: "'The little dog laughs to see such fun and the dish run away with spoon.'"

The philosopher. Insulted once too many times is not done with her yet: "Miss I have one more. How come them won't teach we anything bout Africa!"

"What are you talking about boy? Aren't you told that Africa was discovered!"

"But people greet the arriving discoverers Miss?"

"So what?"

"They discover that people live there Miss!"

"You know of the Spanish Galleons?"

"Yes Miss?"

"The Straits like the one named after Magellan?"

"Yes Miss."

"British Aristocracy?"

"Yes Miss."

"And Piracy and the setting of traps the profession entails?"

"Most certainly Miss."

"All of that preceded the discovery of The Dark Continent."

"If it so dark how they see it Miss with bottle light?"

"No you idiot."

"I didn't think so Miss."

"So what you arguing about then?"

"Miss.... Slavery isn't covered Miss?"

"That's for discussion at another level."

Apparently documented in invisible ink, Slavery is never mentioned and Africa could be a sunken continent as far as the books with which we are educated go.

"That's because such books are not in the syllabus. Now I have had enough of you Waxx the subject is closed."

The etiquette of subservience is still being cultivated. It's with diligence and the luck of making it to secondary schools and university that we do learn something about Africa. These institutions are not built for us but are being pried open so that some upful knowledge can trickle down to us. Singers and Rastafarians spreading the word to stamp out the practice are being kept off the airwaves and out of the mainstream.

Classes are split on Thursday afternoons, girls do sewing and boys do gardening; it's the system, tek book or tek book not, school prepares us for life, by teaching us to work till death, gardening and sewing. What exactly is the system telling me. Inspector comes to school once in a blue moon and we have to ensure the books kept just for his inspection look good, farm looks good and the scraps of cloth the girls and few select boys use in sewing class are clean. That's the real game.

Chapter Twelve

RIGHT AFTER GARDENING WE GO TO BATHE in   Baptism Hole. Swimmers dive from the erosion-rounded, sandstone cliff above its placid, kidney-shaped pool, doing headers, belly flops, jackknife and summersault entries. Baptism Hole's original purpose is cleansing us: either as spiritual beings having a human experience or as human beings having a spiritual experience. This afternoon, as we carouse, Froggy, having made his way atop the rock, screams: "Youtman! Youtman! Come look ya!"

"A wha! Wha yu a gallang so bout!"

"One mermaid inna de water!"

"You too lie, whe'e mermaid goin' come from!"

"Me no know but him een ya though"

"Wishart! How shi get here? Walk from sea?"

"Me no' know! But shi een ya though."

Red-eyed, shrivelled fingers Frankie: "Him lie! Me jus dive out de whole thing; no mermaid no in dere."

Froggy replies: "Yu dive over here shi swim over dere!"

Leaving Frankie adds: "Nothing but him shadow."

I hear but curiosity gets the best of me: "Whe it de?"

"You have to come up yasso? Closer fool!"

I procrastinate, but my curiosity gets the best of me.

He inveigles me: "Maasa yu have to come up more."

Cowardly I reply: "Further yu stand the better yu see."

"Massa you too coward."

"Coward man keeps sound bone."

"Not even coward man wouldn't tan so far! Coward bwoy maybe?"

I approach the edge: "All right, show me, show me!"

He shoves me: "See him there, haaaa ha ha…"

I'm a non-swimmer. I start making tracks for shore but the bank rises vertically, the distance remains the same. I go deep; babbles and bubbles of the precious air leave my mouth and nostrils and go skyward through my grasping fingers. I hit bottom and instinctively push for the top. I can see the shimmering surface and can't wait to get there. There is a burning in my chest. I need air. Bad.   Rays of sunlight dance like broken saucers, on the surface, above my head, somewhere among them, a ray of hope; a sort of rhythm develops in my thrashing. The surface is suddenly around my neck. I want to punch Froggy; curse him; choke him; but I'm choking! Befuddlement as to how a friend could do such a thing, knowing full well that his friend cannot swim flood my mind. I feel like getting angry. I want to kick him but not right now; there is a more pressing matter on my hands. Air.

I expel the oxygen-depleted air once to purge the lungs. My eyes race to scan the panorama with an urgent message from my brain: Tell him say him ded. A dripping forehead, wet eyelashes, wet eyelids and wet irises do not lend themselves to decent enough focus to accommodate my brain. And buoyancy needs assistance in order for me to remain on the surface any longer and I'm offering none.

My second gasp is barely completed when my chin hits then breaks the surface. I'm going south again. I realize that panicking won't work. To hurt Froggy, see Mama and Dada again, drink another aerated water, eat another sardine, and hear "A pretty gal me want" again, play with Ackee Red and Canepiece Rat again, see Dimples again, wet the bed again, sit next to Mama in Church on Sunday I need to break this cycle! The water covers my head and the bottom beckons but I must get to the halfway point first! I must do something I've never done. I must get out of this deep water.

I recall from hearsay that a drowning person rises twice and sinks thrice. I'm on my second sinking. Based on the nasally strong desire to respire, the burning oxygen-deprivation I feel in my lungs, the time's fast approaching for me to get some air. That's up top. I'm heading south, to the bottom.

If I sink again, its goodbye, ashes to ashes, wet dus to wet dus, rigor mortis at the tail end of this, mud to mud. Curtains. And I know it. Think swim. Think swim. I need to swim. I visualize Ackee Red swimming, strokes, kicks, simple, the things he does all the time. I decide the doggie paddle is the easiest; it's been explained to me before, when I had much less interest in learning. I hit bottom and kick off, committed that I'll be strokin' soon.

I start the dog paddle and find form --develop a good rhythm-- as I stroke towards the surface, waitin' to exhale. I gasp when I bust through, exhale big, and inhale even bigger as my hands, now the hands of a swimmer, constantly pump beneath my chest. When I scrape my chest on the sand and instinctively stand, it hits me, I'm a swimmer. Froggy stands motionless and speechless. Unbelievable, I think to myself. Did I just swim? I don't know but I intend to find out. I wade in to chest deep water, turn around and chuck off towards shore. Doggie style, I'm a swimmer.

I want to kill Froggy but I'm too elated. Nothing but ecstasy, relief, love of life, love of self, love of God, love of fellow man and appreciation for the instrument of my new skill and of a breath of fresh air in my lungs and a sense of heart that wants to explode out of my chest.

We dress quickly and head back to school and friends cursing and congratulating each other. We catch dismissal in progress and go against the mass exodus to get our books.

Students are heading home in all directions. I brag to my friends: "Canepiece Rat guess wha!"

"Wha."

"Maasa me learn fe swim."

"How yu do that?"

"Froggy shub me off the rock…"

"Yu lie. Him do that to yu too?"

I say: "Me sink two time. Decide me naah go down again."

"No mek him get way wid it. Tell yu granny. Dat bway a develop a dutty habit. A killa instinct. Him a

211

go end up a wukhouse."
After dinner Mama heads for Froggy's house with me in tow: "Miss Carty a need to talk to yu."

"What is it Miss Iris?"

"Little disturbing news bring me here."

"Is it something I can help you with Miss Iris."

"I think it is maam… it involves your son."

"Have a seat Miss Iris."

"Thanks maam but a must get to the point."

"Sure Miss Iris."

"Him nearly drown me one grandson round a Baptism Hole an kno full well say him can't swim."

"No, not my boy… Froggy come here…."

"Yes Mama!"

Mama: "Push him off o de rock could kill me boy!"

"You push Youtman off the rock today?"

"Yes maam."

"Did you know that he couldn't swim?"

"Yes'n."

"So why you do it?"

"Nothing maam."

"Go bring me my strap."

"Yes'n."

"Miss Iris, I will make sure him pay for it."

"Yes maam."

* * *

212

Impending doom is announced with a "Cyar a come!" And the warning is relayed though sometimes not as fast as the car. Scared, the student body flees; those unable to escape become compact along both embankments until the car goes by. Occasionally, an indecisive kid will suddenly see more safety on the opposite embankment. When Brown Man's miscalculation leads to his sharing the same space with the front of a moving car, his brain swelling, internal organs ruptured departure etched; permanent memories in the minds of those of us witnessing this vehicular snuffing-out of his brief life as a result of: The Opposite Embankment Syndrome: TOES. TOES is directly proportional to another behavioural condition: the Increased Distance Extrapolation Area: IDEA syndrome. It's been proven that the further from the beaten path a kid lives, the greater the possibility that he/she will be afraid of motor vehicle. Brown-man had a rather brief life. The din of an internal combustion engine always traumatizes him. Predisposed to TOES and an IDEA or two along the road, he loses the battle with gravity, which, to us, is still an unknown entity.

The BLACKHEART man brings road-going events to heart-stopping halts. Slowpokes are better off as non-participating curb-huggers. Those of us with 'phobia' for middle name key on the signature of

Terrence R. E. Burey

approaching vehicles, which we speculate, could be his conveyance. The mere utterance of the name causes the heebie-jeebies. Scares the be-Jesus out of us. His suspected approach is relayed up and down the road, each report more frenzied. The effect: an immediate evacuation of the roadway. In the road clearing process, it is every man for himself. The foliage becomes our friend, the river our ally. Should the need arise, one scampers into clutches of Guinea grass or disappear into the orange or coffee fields flanking more student friendly embankments. We flee down sheer cliffs; become cliff-hangers extraordinaire. Hard pressed, some of us have even made it clean through the fence into Thunder, the bad bull's pasture without breaking stride. We jump into the river, skip stones to get to the other side, stones farther apart than on hopscotch, in one single, unstudied, unrehearsed leap.

The visibly eroding areas are never good places to be when the blackheart man is coming. Silent prayers beseech The Father to let us, if we must, run into him at more favourable --for us-- portions of the road. To hear Mongoose tell it: Him only need to look into you eye! Him freeze you right where you stand up!

"Jeezas Gad," hollers Bull, "Den wha' happen!"

"Him come out of him cyar, shove his hand in you chest, rip your heart out, and nyam it!"

He is yet to be positively ID'd but there are abundant accurate descriptions of him. They are uncommon in many ways. But his colour --in keeping with the Anglo-Saxon way of depicting negative things is in keeping with Blacklisting, Blackballed, Black Friday, Blackouts and Black Magic-- specifically the colour of his heart, is unquestioned.

Most evening's, fights are a part of the jaunt home. Earlier schoolyard differences, having been brought to premature ends by the utterance of the word TEACHER during recess, are automatically billed for termination on the way home, hastened to fistical conclusions by set-on's in tightly corralling parties who create tiny circles for the action. Instigators with more anger than the participants thrust palmable pebbles in-between the combatants with the threat: The baddest cock box out this and tek a touch. A quick instigator's hand dismisses any reticence between the enemies. The fight underway, punishing instructions are commonly voiced to the participants --'im an 'im or she an she, as well as 'im an' she-- "Lick 'im! Kick 'im! Fall 'im! Choke out 'im granny! Buss up him blow wow! Grab him by de giznick! Lick him innna him gut hole! T'ump 'im inna 'im ears gad!"

Bullfrog, Cou'n Mary's grandson, has a problem with my brilliance and constantly picks on me. Clover,

215

my cousin through some unclear family dynamics makes it telepathically clear: I got your back, voices, "If him ever touch you me kill him." She's had enough of his bullying me, puts the word in evening recess that the fight has taken a personal turn, it is now hers. She confuses him with her southpaw style and "buss him shut." A week later, because 'her sister comes to visit from Red Hills,' she begins her typical few consecutive days per month absence school. Bullfrog is the first to notice. He spread the word during fight announcement time, evening recess that he will beat me up. Ackee Red and Canepiece-Rat immediately take me through a boxing clinic.

Ackee Red: "Him like punch people in the mouth so me going show you how to block him!"

"If you can't beat him we wi jump in and save you."

I say: "Ackee Red, just take the fight from now nuh man?"

"No man, you can beat him, just do as we tell you."

Last bell rings. My heart is in my mouth. We go through the benediction: "Lighten our darkness...." I can't mutter a word. Canepiece-Rat takes my books. The enemy catches up to me; instigates with a barrage of assaults: "Yu black like tar pot." I have my backitive, so I answer: "Yea? Black is fancy, mallata is dog."

"A goin' beat yu till yu sof' like porridge."

"Yu feel yu strength, head big like fe wharf dog."

"And yu goin fin out whe watah walk go a pumpkin belly."

"Yu huff an' puff but yu can't blow me down!"

"If you think yu bad touch a button."

I know that I'm not bad so I don't even look at his buttons. The instigators have had enough of the posturing. So Four-can, named because he cycles through the standard milk powder line four times before everyone else is served for the first time by the cafeteria staff on Friday afternoons, but who nobody dares to report or confront or call four-can to his face, quickly picks up a little rock, shoves it in-between us and says, "The baddest cock box out dis and take a touch."

Lizard-Lip, a.k.a. Bullfrog, acquired his name in one of his fights, (too far back to recall which one exactly, when he got punched in his mouth so many times, we thought he had no lip left) because him so bad, box it out and shove my right shoulder. Just like in practice, I shove him hard in his stomach, forcing him off balance backwards. Keeping my arms close to my torso, fists protecting my face, I start swaying my arms, in a windshield wiper-like fashion, to and fro in front of my face. He swings at me, I block his punches with my forearms. The ever-thickening throng shouts: "Fight, fight."

I focus on his face. All else is a blur. The roaring crowd goes deathly silent. I'm in the zone. My zone. Ackee Red's yelling, "Go for the jaw with the uppercut right, duck, go for the belly, go for the ears-god," but I don't hear him. Fists fly, as I release a barrage and he starts backing into the crowd, throwing less and less at me, of what's hitting, most reach my arms but lack the sensation of pain I so dreaded.

Most people like an underdog, so my friends and others are rooting me on, now I can hear dem, "Saw it yu fool yu never go a school to learn the rule, lick 'im, lick him Youtman, lick him," I have the moral support I need to "kick ass and take names." Friends shout encouragement to him as well. It's difficult to tell who is for whom: "…lick him, kick him, choke him, thump him, cratch him and lick him inna him gutside, lick out him gut hole…"

I accidentally connect one to his nose and pain rushes to his brain. His feet are told to flee as his brain sensing defeat instructs, he turns to run but is boxed in. I lay a couple more in the centre of his back, windmill style, for good measure. Crouching to evade the barrage, he turns to look at me and wipes the blood trickling from the right hook induced rupture to his left nostril. Seeing fear in his eyes and his drooping arms that say 'I concede' I back off.

We both learn valuable lessons; mine; even though the odds of winning may seem too long, try to, you just might. As the spectators disperse, my friends pat me on the back harder than some of the punches that connected. They make me feel very, very good, "Boy, me tell you say you could beat him! Watch de!"

"You see whaapen! You buss him nose!"

"Where all that skill come from boy!"

As friends, the next day we hear the rumour: "Rematch!"

He timidly asks, "You want fight me again?"

"No sar! You want fight me?"

"Fe wha'? You beat me a'ready?"

I ask, "So Bullfrog why you always pick on me so man?"

"You have too much sense, always clapping yu finger, answerin' question, teecha like you more than me."

"Kiss me neck! Lizard-lip, a that you don't like me for!"

"Teecha suppose to prefer me, me brown with straight nose and you black like tar pot, nose look like bammie presser."

"But Jeezas peace, anybody hear me dyin' trial!" We are getting ready to roll again, but unsure of my second win potential, I philosophise, "Yu know what? Dem say Word is win' but blow is unkind' mek it res'. Yu hear?"

"But you black like wha'! Them say nothing black never good. How come teecha like you more than me?"

"Massa mek me tell you something, black a fancy but malatta a dawg! And stick an' stone can break my bone but your words, they can't harm me." I have my first put down based on the colour thing. Which proves we aren't born with the racism thing. It's adopted along the journey we know as life.

Chapter Thirteen

MY FATHER VISITS AGAIN ON MY BIRTHDAY and raises my passion for things automotive. My interest precipitates a lesson on automobiles. Happy to oblige, he points out, describes and gives reasons for engine compartment components and explains the purpose for and the use of more parts and processes than I can retain. Overwhelmed, I experience initial sensory overload. More gifts. Similar poses. More letters. More pictures to collect house-fly excrements while clipped around the periphery of the bureau mirror. I am eight now. A discussion brews among Mama,

Dada and he, as to my rapid advancement through the lower school. Mama informs him of a meeting initiated by headmaster one Sunday after church: "Me son me mindin me own business when lo and behold Headteecha call me over and tell me say him perform well above par!" Whatever par is.

He stands: "Say what! The boy is doing good!"

"You sister Esther is vice-principal now, right?"

"Yes Mama."

Mama: "See if she want to finish him up. He will have the best chance to pass common entrance…."

"Yes Mama, that way we can get him into a good secondary school, something I never got to do…"

"Willie think him get your brain."

Dada chimes in: "Him is you spitting image too!"

"He should go to H.C. Them deny me a place!"

"You deny Jasmine... wanted to kill you and she! If you concentrated on the school problem…"

He ignores Dada, "Not their philosophy to school us."

Dada constantly reinforces me to 'tek book,' his way of saying: do your lessons. Books must really do something to you because most times that someone passes in a pretty car that catches Mama's eye, she says, "It's because them take book why them can drive past in such a boasy car!" Be they Doctor, Fireman, Principal, Insurance Salesman or Inspector; anything at all, Mama and Dada say it's because them take book. Because I love cars I know I'm going to take book.

To help me develop a meaningful vocabulary, he assigns me the job of village voice. I read our newspaper, to gatherings. I am the media's voice for the illiterates, reading all headlines then following with articles sparking the greatest interest. Initially, I spell more of the multi-syllabic words than I can pronounce. He encourages my phonetic attempts. Naturally, the more I read, the more proficient I become. He decides which latecomers merit re-readings, "Sonny, read so and so again so Maas Joe can hear it." My largest audience is on Saturday mornings, the rest day, following the Monday to Friday grind. Those bringing up the rear join the newscast in progress. Live paper.

Reading is one; comprehension is a whole different ballgame. Messenger included. I am elevated to personal assistant to those feigning poor sight. Sadly, these individuals can see their names on a bulla cake and nyam it unrecognized. In visible but verbal-eaves-dropping-challenged sequestration under the Poinciana tree, I learn more than is necessarily pertinent via their poorly written letters from our societal-bar-met barely literate relatives. It's an integral part of these sessions that I also pen thank you's and pleas for more money. To them I owe my grasp of reading cursive at such an early age. I try to respond to such letters in kind and is therefore deliberate in my efforts and before long, I am a cursive writing maniac. My comprehension skills kick in. My letter writing services peak prior to all the religious and national festivities. Harvest at any local church incites special begging for dresses, shoes, hats and money on cards for an organ, piano, pews or other pet projects. Emancipation day, which, in most parts of the island, will soon be replaced by Independence festivities, causes special begging for? You guessed it, blouse and skirt and pants and shirt along with shoes, hats and money. Christmas requires special begging for more of the same plus toys.

Seasonal road repairs provide income for affiliates of the ruling political party. The road through town is being paved. The qualification for positions on the road crew is a letter of introduction to the 'super' at the Public Works Department. Roadwork crews take pride in maintaining their stretches, remove erosion deposits to deny wild grasses their over-taking growth and by so doing, take even an inch of the already narrow, barely adequate pavement.

*   *   *

"Esther! Me first boy a show promise!"

"Whey you a talk bout boy?"

"Headmaster tell Aunt Iris him show promise!"

"Poh! That no surprise me!"

"What you mean gal!"

"De ly bway tek de brains from yu bway!"

"Think you can take him and finish him?"

"Couldn't bring you up, a de leas' me can do."

Two Fridays' hence Mama and I visit to confirm the transition. It is also a dry run, for me. Alls one has to do is show promise then sign on to become a member of the next G.E.D. --gypsy education degeneration.

Dada: "Iris Oh!"

"Yes Willie."

"We have to put together one box for Esther!"

"It's old as the hills. On any visit, I know to bring a little something go give them Willie."

We leave early on the early bus and connect in Christiana's terminus, but will not depart for an hour. The driver is in a bar across the street ensuring that he will be driving while intoxicated. We take our seats and wait. I sit away from Mama across from the centre of operations to learn more. The driver approaches with the gait of a polio victim. Forty years of long days in a dead-end job. He climbs aboard by swinging his personal door open and using the driver side front tire as a two rung ladder and the base of his doorway, his overcompensating right foot, flexed at the ankle claws forward as if trying to cover more ground than he actually does. Seated, he warms the glow plugs of his diesel engine for about a minute and once he fires up the motor, he lets it sit there at a fast idle to get her up to operating temperature and also to increase the compressed air's pounds per square inch (psi) which is vital as it operates the brakes and the horn. We depart and I am a transfixed pupil.

For the next nineteen miles we gain altitude like helium-filled dirigibles. We continue on a serpentine, northerly heading through Dunip, Lorrimers, Lowe River, Wait A Bit, Stettin and The Alps we average six miles per hour before the bus slows to a crawl. This road crosses the backbone of the island in the Cockpit Country and is classic yard style road: very winding. (With two bus trips under my belt I'm like any new frequent-flyer club member with two flights, two international flights with a four hour lay-over in an airport lounge, under my belt: An expert on the region.) Drop-short's loss of the relaxed look telegraphs to a keen observer, that something's up. The route familiar passengers find religion, and the bus erupts in song.

We're a spiritual revival on wheels, singing sacred sankies being raised and joined by pockets of passengers like they're going out of style. A vocalist leads, some passengers shake tambourines and cymbals; others unhand handkerchiefs and purses and handclap their way into the orchestra. Mama jumps in with both feet. Though most men aren't participating in the activity, I seem to be on a bus filled with flocks headed to a religious revival. In actuality, we need to descend from the pinnacle of a mountain. Out of one corner, he is winding the wheel in the other direction, selecting yet another gear, making room for an approaching vehicle to pass on a road that seems too small for the bus as it is. He approaches a corner that sits on the edge of a cliff with a shear drop of five hundred feet. Buses and trucks must back-up in order to successfully negotiate this corner and to say we approach it gingerly is an understatement. Collectively they sound ready to meet The Maker, tomorrow anyway, as is evidenced by the sanky de jour:

"One bright morn when the fight is o'er
I'll fly away
[Unintelligible discord] tha' great celestial shore
I'll fly away."

At the mid-turn, he stops to select reverse, a pocket of passengers' pipes in,

227

"Away on the mountain, wild and bare

Aaawaay from tha Teender Shepherd's care…"

Baaaaad. Backing up, in song an ultimatum is given,

"Yu better get right with Gad… do it now,

At the cross of Jesus I'll lay my burden down…"

To negotiate it, Drop Short, by breaking the 'no downhill usage of air horn rule' alerts all oncoming traffic with three long blasts of the klaxon; goes down, un-Yard-like in the box, non-sequentially crosses the gate: minimalistically selects two gears including second low where he stays then goes as close as he can to our side of the road. With all the strength he can muster, he manipulates the difficult manual steering, puts in all the available lock. No room for error. The bus is dead quiet. We are at the apology for a retaining wall and he hangs the left fender over it, the front tire at a point that barely precedes that point of no return which to me seems to be three quarters the way through space, to the other peak-defined horizon in full song of the engine and the once again crooning congregation. He chases the gear selector lever and after rocking it several times to the left and right in a range-of-motion cipher, he selects reverse. He half-masts the clutch and while using that to keep the bus stationary and without stalling the engine releases the brake pedal, gives her gas --diesel-- and avoiding any sudden moves disruptive to the teetering load in the carrier, to take her backwards. The singing continues as he prepares for final approach,

"In His hands, He's got the whole world…"
Steady as she goes while inputting the opposite lock with a typical manual steering that reacts in single digit radians to ten-degree inputs, points the back end on a new trajectory. The singing in back is conflicting with

"…Saviour pilot me, let me to thy bosom fly…"

In first gear he takes her round the bend as passengers visually inspired by the sheer rock faces raise:

"Rock of ages cleft for me…"
The middle section raises,

"Why worry when you can pray
Just ask Jesus He will lead the way…"

The successful negotiation is not lost on the bipartisan congregation: It brings full applause and an abrupt end to the gospel showcase. It's all downhill from here. Sawyers, the village, soon swallows us in her shadows that the higher heights project. Tributary-lets cause large potholes in the softened narrow pavement at the base of sheer constellation bound rock faces. Through Litchfield, Barbeque Bottom and Kinloss, we lose more passengers than we gain. In the encapsulating darkness I am clueless as to where in creation we are.

We arrive in Duncans and alight by Crest theatre in the glow of an electric moon standing on a stick. The astute sideman unerringly retrieves our box from the bus' carrier then three thuds ricocheting off the side of Crest Theatre accompany his audible: "Go-so bus." We stand back and watch, as the bus, being swallowed up in the darkness, disappears around the town-exiting bend. Smukums, Dimples-like in more ways than one, in her mid teens is here to meet us. Because of the distinct family resemblance she walks up to us with a dimpled smile and says,

"Hi, you must be Youtman?" Loudly but because of the altitude induced temporary hearing loss the verbiage registers in a soft voice.
And to Mama, "You must be Aunt 'I'?"

"Yes me dear and who are you?" Mama asks. Smukums replies: "I am Dell maam May's daughter."

"I remember you as a little something in town. Boy oh boy yu grow into a nice young lady. And is so yu look like yu madda when she was a teenager. It is good to see you."

"Thank you Aunt I."
I reach for the box, "Youtman that seems a bit heavy for you, I'll take it."

"Okay," I say, "It is kinda heavy!" Having carried it before but not complaining about the help. Leaving town Smukums uses her flashlight to cut the darkness which is punctuated by few homes with their veranda lights on.

"So how was the bus ride Aunt I?"

"We had to take two my love."

"Really! How were they?"

"Not bad."

A couple of passing boys recognize the bounce of the flashlight beam on the pavement and boys being boys cannot resist making a flirting comment,

"Smukums! A wha' you de do out so late?"

"That's for me to know and you to find out."

"Gal you de romp rough."

"Romping! What with?"

The new 'de do' in the dialect gets my attention, so as soon as they were out of earshot I ask Smukums what's up with the "de do" thing? She explains that for the most part it's a substitution for "is" or "are" and as a by-the-way it works for plain "do" as well.

"Smukums!"

"Yes Youtman."

"What is all them little fire in the yard them?"

Mama, the sudden Gramatical Expert is on me like stink on faeces, "Boy speak properly!"

"Yes Mama." How? I wonder.

Smukums explains, "That's dried cow dung burning!"
A linguistically correct, collective 'Oh' greets her from
Mama and I. Then she continues,

"Its smoke repels mosquitoes from the homes."

"That's your mosquito destroyer!" Cow dung!
I think to myself.

"Yes," she says proudly.

"We buy ours at the shop!" I pipe in, querying,
"It make from the same thing Mama?"

"A don't know, but a don't think so me son."
Little do I know that I am making inquiries into one of
my chores --upcoming dung collector. A church brother
going the other way, in the soft afterglow of a lone
streetlight says hello, "A you that Smukums!"

"Yes it is."

"A wha' you de do out so late?"

"I went to meet my cousin off the bus."

"Praise The Lord. Goodnight everybody."

"Goodnight brother. Praise God." Mama chimes
in, recognizing and appreciating his solidarity.

"Me notice that you don't talk Patois to him?"

"Patois is not completely forbidden in our house
but you could get a spanking for speaking it."

"Why that?" I ask. It is about all I ever speak.

She responds, "Being the family we are in the town, you know, with Brother G a well-respected minister and Aunty a teacher and Vice Principal at school, they expect a certain decorum from us."

"I see. What's decorum?" I can't remember even reading that one in the newspaper, come to think of it; it's a lucky thing I used to read the paper or I would'a salt. She ignores my question and points out the school. Mama gives it a full going over, at least as much as the light radiating from the streetlights allows, then says, "Oh it looks really nice."

"That's the playing field as you can see," she says pointing, "...and the classroom here is Auntie's."

"Hhhmmm."

"And down there by the bougainvillea are both the Principal and Vice Principal's office, they refer to that as the Administration wing because it has the secretary, infirmary and all that stuff."

I escape criticism: "It put fe we school to shame."

"Is that right! Aunty will be pleased to hear that."

I couldn't help but ask, "You have river near?"

"No but we have the sea. Can you swim?

The expert I am by now I answer, "But must! Sorry. Yes I can." Before Mama bludgeons me with her purse.

"The sea must be pretty close?" Mama asks.

"Yes it is Aunt I; it's just beyond the hill."

Terrence R. E. Burey

"What hill?" I ask.

Pointing she says, "See those lights going higher and higher over there!"

"Yes Smukums."

"Oh! I thought so, I can smell it."

Sure you can Mama, sure you can, I say to myself.

"We're going onto this little side road and it will be the first gate on the left."

"Smukums!"

"Yes Youtman!"

"A can ask you a question?"

"Sure thing family, ask away…"

"How you know so much words?"

"Reading is my passion."

"What that mean?"

"I love to read."

"A see!"

"And I learn lots of new words that way."

"So where does this nylon road go?" I ask, checking my grammar on the fly.

She responds in proper diction, "In front of us to Kingston, behind us, to Montego Bay."

"Straight?"

"No, thru towns you'll learn about in Geography."

"Oh."

We arrive at the manse and three pedigree-mongrels rush towards the gate. Smukums commands them, "Go back in the yard."
She commands them, using very thought-provoking names: Blackie, Brownie and Spot. I want to burst out laughing but choke it back.

"Man those are original; who named the dogs?"

"I did," Smukums says, adding; "Keeps it simple." No mistaking which is which, that's for sure.

"I see," I say then remain quiet without realizing I'd vocalized the first part, and adding nothing else.

"See what," Smukums queries.

"The wire on the gate is to keep the dogs in."
Serious bloodhounds that they are, I think to myself. It suddenly dawns on me, we closed a gate behind us, I start thinking: Well hell's bells, I'll be cloistered behind a real live and in the flesh, welded double hung wrought iron gate on concrete posts. No more right at the roadside for me."
The veranda light is on and flowers jostling for position border the driveway and are held in check with conch shells. A breadfruit tree on the left and a huge avocado tree on the right lay deep in the floral recesses, which are unrecognizable in the ambient light. Sweet sop, naesberry and pomegranate trees along with other fruit trees of every description peer from the dark and grasp

a little of the light to exhibit themselves. Somebody 'round here got a few green thumbs.

We walk about fifty yards to the intimate veranda where Aunty and Minister are sunken in Adirondack style chairs. They are still invisible from my vantage point because of something to do with Physics and light shining directly into our eyes. Class has some strange rules, one of them being that if you think you are higher on the social scale than someone else then you don't rise up in a hurry to greet him or her, you get up when you're good and ready. But even in front of class, smoke from the dry cow dung wafts around us. And is inhaled by all as class respires just like the rest of us.

With that song it isn't until Mama and Smukums climb the steps onto the veranda that our host and hostess rise to greet us, a warm handshake from the God-fearing practitioner and a hug from the blood. We barely got in the salutations before the man of the cloth announces,

"Well I think a word of prayer is necessary! God brought you from far! Anything could have befallen you along the way!" He offers the supplication, "Lord thank you for letting these, two of your humble servants have a safe trip. Thou knowest God, that anything could have befallen them along the way! Dear

Jesus, many have left home today and will never return. Oh Jesus, they will today Father either meet you or face eternal damnation instead! Sitting at the right hand of The Father we hope that You have mercy on such souls. But you God, in Your tender mercies, brought our beloved souls safely here. Father God, a pray that if there are any among us, not yet ready to meet you Father, You, as the one that knows all, will have them open their heart and soul, like Your Son Jesus did, Father God, to meet You, Father God, on that glorious morn. But that you instil upon them not to put it off Dear God, as we know not the minute or the hour that we shall be called. I pray that You the creator, create an atmosphere of fellowship, Father God, because Thou see-est and Thou knowest, why we meet oh Father in heaven. I ask that you guide and direct our every move, our every action and decision Father. For Thou, Oh Gaad, knowest that we dare not make a decision, without first taking it to you Jesus, Lord and Father, in prayer. In supplication Gaad... A pray that you will grant them a pleasant stay, Father God. Father we pray for the sick and shut in tonight Lord, Sister Dawkins and Sister Bright. Pray that you will bring a speedy recovery to the ill you want to have such a recovery Lord. Lord I think of Sister Maxwell. Father we pray for those having no peace in their hearts Father, those whose leaders lack the love to have their nations realize peace. Father we pray for those who have lost loved ones in wars tonight; we pray that their hearts were filled with love Lord. We pray that they knew you Father, so that they too will experience everlasting life. We pray for those that don't yet know Your Name Father Gaad we pray will know of your wonderful Name soon. Father Gaad we leave it all in Your Hands Father, we leave the whole world in Your Hands. In Your Son Crise Jeezas Name we pray. As well as in Thy Name! Amen and Aman."

We are pointed to the indoor plumbing to get all washed up. The grousing gormandiser at the head of the table minces no words. He masticates the food and seems capable of putting it all away. Mastication is uppermost in his mind. Once burped and fed, the man has a much better personality. The adults retreat to the living room for conversation. Smukums introduces me to the other members of my new family. All ended up here for the same purpose. I'm the only boy among four girls and I am related to the oldest three; the youngest has me beat by two years. I listen as they describe life in the manse. I am shown the church next door and soon realize that it plays a very large roll in our lives. Mama joyfully says, "Thank The Lord it can't do nutten but help yu to get a better heddication."

Saturday starts with consciousness-awakening prayers at five. It takes my cousin Daisy, Miss kitchen duties, the better part of an hour to bring the wood-burning wrought iron stove up to temperature and another hour to produce the dinner style meal the man of the house desires. We pray and have breakfast.

A whirlwind of faces and information on church members who stop are thrown at me. Some bring food from their farms. I'm introduced around, informally interviewed and welcomed into the fold. I'm told to go with Tiny, the adoptee, to uproot water grass by the pond for rabbit food. Thoughts flash through my mind about a match made in heaven, but I'm in a Christian home. But they recur.

Then it's off with Smukums to the grocery shop, the market and bakery in town and with Daisy to get wood for the chimney vented cooking stove.

I'm a part of a national pastime, It's decided; set in stone; the way parents and guardians alike, in the name of education won't give a second thought to the idea of school transfers uproot and transfer children 'showing promise' in things academic. Such a display of brilliance creates an odyssey for the child, chasing the name-droppings of those teachers --preferably a principal-- capable of bringing out the best in each of us. Needless to say, all parents sending their children away are expecting a graduate in the top of their class in an excellent field. As to what that field is, neither they nor the child have a clue and mentors are hard to find, so it is up to the teacher, who is not necessarily a mentor, to decipher everyone's mind and gear them towards the right field.

Most times the teachers are just as clueless, except to tell you to become a teacher. The field is very limited. The piece of The Rock that I know gears children to two fields, well three fields actually, teaching, nursing and farming. For that choice, kids are moved around on a coded slave trade; some children's parents and guardians think one way: Good schooling at all costs. At the end of the day you sometimes wonder "Oh what a price!" It's psychologically damaging.

The remainder of the afternoon is a whirlwind of faces and information; it duplicates the morning. Late evening, Tiny and I enjoy the half-mile walk to go uproot more watergrass by the secluded pond. I like this already, but for all the wrong reasons. Not. Saturday night prayers. Dinner. Prayers.

Sunday morning we awake, prayer; breakfast, prayer; then Sunday school and morning service at the Church beyond the dual leather-strap-hinged gate. Before and after Sunday school I am the object of whispered introductions, the recipient of questions peppered with "de do": Yu de go? Yu de come? Wha yu de do? Wha yu de say. How long yu de stay? Following worship services, visitors practically line up at the Tabernacle/Manse separating gate shouting: Hole dawg! Then, finding time away from complementing minister on a wonderful service, inquisitively converse with me, with a view to get the real meat on who I am. Leaves are added to the dining table and prayer precedes a large dinner. Tiny and I go to get water grass for the rabbits and I like the direction our conversation takes. Mama and I enjoy this unplanned extra day of north coast hospitality because the bus does not operate on Sundays. We depart Monday morning after prayer. Come end of this term I'm off to Auntie.

Beatrice stop giving milk again and Ackee Red and I go to Uncle Chris. We have just collected our milk when the westbound bus makes a one stop right in front of us. We look at each other and it is too good to resist. We are close to school a mile south of home. We'd save half the walk. It's one thing to listen to your friend, another to judge distance when the speed at which it is being covered is different from the way it's covered underfoot. The image of missing the turn-and-bailing-off point, passing my home like that is not a pretty one. We dare not go all the way home this way; wi parents will beat us to death. Over the din, Ackee

Red coaches me about the appropriate bailing off point; half way through his diatribe it's feeling like an eternity, paranoia is setting in. I see familiar embankments and a section where the river runs next to the road without any kind of retention wall, up a small hill down the other side, we're doing well, we should be at the 'S' bend any minute. Ackee Red senses my paranoia and insists that I don't jump until he tells me. The decreasing motivation brings my chest into contact with the metal ladder and I think: yes, this is it. We get to Breadfruit Crop's corner, Maas Dad to his face, "We going to hop off… right sah!" I barely feel the centrifugal force as the driver begins negotiating the corner. Inputting the first lock, the bus is still going too fast for us to hop off, dust is swirling around us, trees are going backwards; I'm wondering if this is death staring me in the face: "When he goes in the gearbox get ready, we have to wait till he negotiates the first portion of the corner." I look down through the dust to the ground. I suddenly realize that the ground is going even faster than the trees. Jesus Christ me ded, I wonder to myself. He senses the panic.

"Youtman no do nutten till me tell you."

"Awright."

The minute's nigh. I get nervous. This is it. I'm overpowered by the urge to get off.

I bail. Just as I release my grip Ackee Red shouts out, "No' yet, no' yet Youtman." I'm already falling backwards and must move my feet so that I land vertically with my milk bottle in my right hand. I focus on his face now being enveloped in a cloud of dust, yelling but not saying a word. I remember to run so I run after the bus.

This time, however, the big hand of centrifugal force jumps into the mix, shoving me sideways. The earth comes up to greet me and I instinctively hold the milk bottle far away from our jarring but surprisingly unfeeling rendezvous point, my left side. I inhale heavy, tyre-served-marl-dust and taste the flying particles that find their way into my open mouth.

I body surf towards the embankment, which, unlike the curving road that the bus tyres are following, lies straight ahead. The curbside placement of the ladder makes it a short trip to and through the built up, rough ridge of gravels at roadside.

Ackee Red having reached the more advantageous point in the centre of the two turns, where the bus travels at its slowest and where less physical forces are acting on it, as it has to change directions completely and as a result must travel at its slowest speed in a straight line for a little while, bails off and rushes back. His first words are like those of a parent:

"Don't me tell yu to wait till me tell yu fe jump man, rahtid cup bwoy yu could'a kill y'uself? You get cut?" The pain impairs my hearing so he repeats himself: "Me say if yu get cut nowhere?"

Pain begins to confirm my injuries: "Yea, 'pon my side and my elbow. Hold me milk fe me."

We check the damaged sectors; I'm down to the pelvis white: Cartilage. Discovery on the left hip, a couple small pieces of marl stuck in my left palm close to the wrist. Nothing a little homemade remedy can't fix. I get a little saliva and dab the hip first and then the palm. A couple pebbles are embedded; Ackee Red picks them out with a macka from a lime tree in the nearby property, which coincidentally belongs to his dad.

"Lucky ting de milk in you right hand."

"Me wud find wey water walk go punkin belly."

"You can say that again!"

"Mek me see if me can walk. Oh God!"

"A what?"

"Me hips feel like it broke."

"You lucky a only that."

"Lucky!"

"You could'a rolled into the river."

"Over the bankin?"

"Over the bankin."

"You mad as shad."

"What you jump so soon for?"

"Me no know."

"Even Canute slow down'round two corner…"

"So!"

"Mek me finish!"

"Me elbow!"

"Every driver have to almost stop in a de middle to make the steering wheel wine back to the middle then wrap up fe get the other side."

"Oh! That's why me tell yu fe wait till me tell yu when fe hop off Bredgin!"

"Yea. You lucky say the backle never bruk and de milk dash way, that would a be de mash-a-laa!"

"Yu got that right me fr'en'."

At the exit point of the second corner, there is a little track that leads to the river; we go down there to clean up my wounds and then continue home, me under severe mouthing. We naturally decide to keep it to ourselves. It is tough sitting for breakfast and in church but I manage. Another old adage say's: "All's well that ends well!" But this incident definitely is not ended yet.

On the bus' return journey, a woman from an adjoining village does the responsible thing the African in us demands; she asks the driver for a one stop: "Tailah yu need to carry yu boy go a Doctor a morning!"

"A what yu talkin bout missis?"

"Him nearly dead round a tunnin this morning!"

"Say warrah!"

"Him drap offa de bus ledder!"

"Yu lie!"

"No sah! Only Massa Gad save him."

"Thank you very much Miss Roper."

As the bus departs, I am frozen in position next to him and he searches for appropriate artillery to correct my life-threatening indiscretion. He finds the curved stick he uses to cut the contours into fabrics for slacks. The first swipe across my back carries the aroma of vengeance and my scapula deflects it away from my still smarting, low back. I run. He goes easy on me, being his favourite and all, and so, other than to my pride, I escape further damage. He harbours no hate and wants to see the wounds so he can make a damage assessment.

Chapter Fourteen

I TELL MY FRIENDS OF THE IMMINENT MOVE and soon the entire district seems aware. Some schoolmates are supportive. Mama insists I write to inform Auntie that I reached home safely. I write: Dear Auntie, I reached home safely... I had such fun... I look forward... Everyone sends their love... thanks in advance....

Soon home will be any ending point of my bus ride.

Two Sundays later Baba Laiza grabs my attention. I find salvation during alter call following his out of season lesson: Joel 3:13 "Put ye in the sickle, for the harvest is ripe." I feel a hot rush, during alter calls rendition:

"Just as I am without one plea…"

The next morning word of my salvation is campus wide. I walk the walk, talk the talk and try to think the thoughts. Pure thoughts. Forehead's disrobed body creeps into my noggin. I quickly erase it with a silent flogging: God forgive me. Schoolmates certify my spirituality. Ackee Red is the first one; he slaps me on one cheek. My eyes wide with astonishment he says: "Turn the other cheek."

I angrily ask him," Why should I do that? "

"A yu a de Christian," he sneers.

"I did not bother you! Why yu a 'box' me? "

He politely says: "The Bible says when someone hits you on one cheek you should turn the other one."

I want to hit him but pressure from Duck Foots' fist reaches my back. I hide, to save "God Forgive Me's." My preoccupation with seeking forgiveness distracts me from my academics. I score poorly on quizzes. At home, sinners besiege me. I am inspired to read The Bible from Genesis to Revelation. The process enlightens me to a new form of living: choreless existence. Mama's pride bag is at the point of bursting. She encourages, "Ask me to pronounce any word that you don't get Sonny!"

"Yes Mama."

I am fascinated by 'begat', and its meaning. I'm on a begat scan. Biblical folks sure did a lot of begatting, boy howdy. When wives can't begat they lay maids with their husbands, then they lay awake nights, hoping that after the liaisons main thrust, to do the begattin, they do some intimate fegattin. At the river, when I go to bathe, my body looks holier. Suspended on the pew above the red straw dye floor, I get a whole new grasp on The Word. I do a lot less drifting, except of course for eleven o'clock bus' stop at school gate; a fascination with Mama's fan; I am unaware, and so is she, that in the more advanced society west of our island, the speed at which she oscillates her wrist sends messages to the men around her. Her slow rate rightfully indicate she is married; a hurried swing, a haste of the bearer to be engaged in activity with a proclivity towards more immediate needs and dropping the fan is an open invitation for a prospect to pick up the bearer. I wonder if Nowee, is at the foot of the hill yet; Sister Freda's drooling in her sleep; the source of some bad gas pewily permeates the pews, the likelihood of a rendezvous under church cellar tomorrow; oops; God forgive me. My thoughts drift to much earlier memorised school required, advancement passages:

Master Willy had a roll in the mud...

This is Mister Joe's yard...

I ponder the mountains horizon effect, foreign to me, its proximity to Heaven? Drift to Maas Joe-Joe's yard, to Banana Ground, Jericho... and back to Peckham. Forehead. Is she going to join her sister in England? Study nursing? We should get past the competition. I must ask her to... God forgive me. I return to the sermon when the non-snoring members stand for the benediction. Parson presses flesh; I shake his hand as one of The Flock... looking forward to my ice cream cone.

Monday trouble doesn't even set like rain
It cascades as trials tribulations and physical pain

In de schoolyard before first bell
Nuff test my faith, tempt me to tell
them go to hell.

Trials and tribulations of the fistical kind
Attempt to break my spine I swear blind
My restraint is bipolar
I don't want lick a girl
And of the boys I get cold shoulder

Under additional attacks I try to be meek
As The Father says turn the other cheek

But tests of my Faith continue fast and furious
By the pain my brain tells me they're injurious
Pounding pressure in my back they maintain
Sounds reverberate to my tympanic membrane

As fluids try to settle in my eardrum
Plucky, the brownin' unsettles my equilibrium
'F you a Christian you can't tump back someone
Lick one cheek means you turn the other one

My mind thinks Christianly unrepeatable stuff
They're testin my faith sure enough
Of what's on my mind I'm sure you get the gist
I won't be long till I start responding with fist

Now comes Beenie, diminutive, older than me
With parson for a father he should let me be
He doesn't want me blurting out things I know
Regardless he spars with words throws a blow

By Tuesday afternoon I am answering fistically
My Christianity is leaving me somewhat gradually
I'm at a crossroads Thursday afternoon
I take a lick from Beenie, a fight erupts soon

251

Fistically there is really no contest
Because I've had as much as I'm gonna digest
He becomes the recipient of terrible blows
Thrown with muscular strength only God knows
I'm punchin in bunches almost at insanity
And yes that is that for my Christianity

        *   *   *

Apprenticeship is a transitory state and Dada experiences his share of turnovers. He trains intensively. With Job-like patience, he thoroughly trains the next and the next, and the next. When they're capable, he assigns them the more mundane parts of the process. Those leaving, abscond, career in hand, to forge for themselves. To the vacant stool comes another student, head hung low, parent in tow and another story much like the past one on their tongue. So said, another of the unending succession of apprentices gets taken under his mentoring wing. Once again, as they can help themselves off they go. The revolving door continues. Wanting to emulate my idol, I want more than anything else to learn the trade. Each time I ask or seem too interested, I am sternly discouraged. Further attempts at learning it will have him invoking the mantra: Trade is only fo' bwoys who don't take book Sonny, so go and tek up yours yuh hear. As for what there is to do when one takes book is another story completely as there is nothing or anyone that informs those of us in this back-o-wall town exactly what to do, or what there is to do, beyond tailoring, dressmaking and agriculture.

The appearance of his big shot clients with this knowledge to impart, if they took the time to impart a little of that knowledge to us, would, do a world of good, to our adults and children, who because of the prevalent illiteracy, have no concept of anything beyond our borders, cause major changes in his itinerary.

These clients reside throughout the island as well as in Canada, England and The States. They bring him fabrics for their custom-built suits. Diligent to a fault, he makes every attempt to accommodate them but his over-commitments sometimes make him late with his deliveries unless he pulls all-nighters for a special client who must catch a ship, a plane, or for locals who must attend a wedding or a graduation.

Once the business of fittings and schedules are done, it's then time to 'go tek a liquor'. Playing good district politics Dada patronizes both imbibing emporiums, Ackee Red's and Top Shop. If I catch his eyes at the right time, I can finagle a "come Sonny," my queue to accompany them to the bar and get my favourite aerated water, but I am always welcome even if the spoken words do not grace his lips. After a few rounds, his not mine, he will send me to tell Mama to get sup'm for them to eat.

Her trade as a dressmaker is relegated to second place, behind her wifely duties. She'll drop everything and in two two's will have him and his entourage burped and fed. They give her the usual comments:

"Laud Miss Iris you' hand is as sweet as ever..."

"'F Willie nuh mine sharp me might stay here."

"Under this kind'a living... me fat like cut puss." The more inebriated: "If him ever start fe skid yu see darling, you jus' mek me know, yu have a place whey me deh anytime." Still unclear is the point of whether she will be wife or just cook.

Chapter Fifteen

LIFE IN THESE PARTS IS NOTHING CLOSE TO the tempo we see on the silver screen. Rich-Man brings free-shows to town often. They entertain and inform us about the fast-paced side of the American lifestyle, but we must struggle to follow the dialogue over the sound of the alternating current (a/c), power-generating unit at the other end of the projector's electrical power cord. Unlike our vast citizenry that moves about at a deliberately slow pace, the stars and extras in these flicks just rush, rush, rush. Cowboys bent for leather, high-tailing it to nowhere, the occupants of luxurious automobiles, whether they depict bank robbers or joy-riders simply going around in circles, travel at bird-speed.

We soak up all this action as it bounces off Ackee Red's shop or the side of our tailor shop with their generally unencumbered view. Either 'silver screen' works, if the other is obstructed by a load of sugarcane, stones or the sawyer-man's lumber.

Rich-Man also rolls explicit films, the most graphic of which is Street Corner. It goes to great lengths in demonstrating the consequences of poor family-planning methods to the futile fertile. Unfortunately they go against the cultural grain and do nothing to stem the local stud tide's rush towards four-star generalship.

In our 'Third World Mentality' we assimilate the coded messages they send us. The films' marketing reps do not mention, nor do our leaders 'cotton on' to the power of subliminal messages. At film speed, slightly better than fourteen frames-per-second --the frequency beyond which our eyes see everything as being in constant motion-- we fall in love with their culture.

With sticks, local sword fighters emulate the silver screen productions of Zorro the Gay Blade, Captain Blood and Robin Hood. As cowboys we cut guns out of wood tote them everywhere we go and Indians, we use bamboo strips to make bows and arrows. Combined we shoot and fight.

*   *   *

Holidays are a break for parents, teachers and guardians. At this time the island adopts full Gypsy mode. Cousins visiting from Kingston provide a special prize to any family; their speakie-spokie-ness draws big crowds, as local yokels press closely to them to absorb the latest slangs and twangs. Guardians derive merit from having these visitors; the women in Church and the men sidling up to the bar take great pride in announcing their additions: 'cousins' without a hint of resemblance hanging out for the holidays.

*   *   *

The New Year holiday is the most conservative one. The women folk who feel the need to worship lead us kids to watch night services; here the New Year finds us in song, prayer, tongues, testimony or nodding off from tiredness or boredom. Hardly a soul in the house can truly say the state in which the New Year found him or her as we all watch, wristwatch-less. Can't afford zilch on our hands but time, but on our minds: anticipation.

*   *   *

Holidays are also a time of high anticipation and our salubrious climate of four distinct seasons: Summer, summer, summer and summer, give us plenty of time to play. Our games remain in vogue year-round.

Team games, one-on-one games and games where it's everyone for one's self. Regardless of the game de jour some people never get picked. The girls only pick rabbit lip Daffodil who we prefer to call Engine, because her teeth resemble the massive chrome bars on the grille of Scrammie's car. Having to stand back and watch most of the time affects her game in a positive way. She beats them all at jax. When they skip rope, she lasts longer than most of them. And Lincoln, we don't want his sore-foot hand on any of our game equipment. Belly-mo with his big navel stutters badly and cannot make the calls in our audible games like chivvy-chase and hide-an-seek without long pregnant pauses.

Presshie and the older boys take turns riding his bicycle at 'bird speed' to set new records. They want to experience speed at its highest and thrills at their wildest while being safe at the same time. Perpetually ringing the bell seemingly guarantees the rider's safety; it also distracts others from their activities making the cyclist the temporary focus as he hastens down the middle of the road.

Romping boys noisily play cricket: at bat, bowling, at slip and in the gully. Good fortune's refusal to smile on our collective plight dictates the use of a substitute to the Wesley Hall ninety miles-per-hour leather-bound oxblood red projectile we carve from a bamboo root.

In our football games either on the road or a designated grassy area we play: On the goalie, with pressure, the centre forward presses with a good pass from his half back while utilising a grapefruit or an empty condensed milk can to score. In these barefoot attempts at stardom, the soles of our feet must be ever so slightly elevated above the road's surface as a kick that's off by a hair will make us pay dear shear epidermis and endodermis.

Playing shark while we bathe in the river truly tests the capacity our lungs.

Hide and go seek, especially the co-ed variety, is our only inspiration for boys aspiring to be doctors with our career path girl nurses.

In marble games of lick and stick each person fires a 'taw' into the dusty ring, scatters portions of the bounty outside the bounds of its five inch diameter, the shooter maintains a bench and batty proximity to the remainder, hopes to be a winner every time. Bounce back, is racquet ball like but with three key exceptions:

no racquets, more players each with a taw sequentially thrown to ricochet off the wall and get close to any previously pitched marble, span the distance with thumb to pinkie or ring finger and acquire as a reward, a marble from its unlucky owner. A rolling game of pitch and spawn in which, for variety we either use large, barely manageable river stones or marbles help to pass the time when we must cover great distances.

Gigue: irresistible wooden faux replica of a top with a ten penny nail or screw driven in and its head filed off and brought to a point is sometimes used to destroy a victim or competitively demonstrate its sleeping ability, seeing whose, once wound up with the requisite piece of english cord and 'dropped,' is able to 'sleep' the longest.

Bunny, a.k.a. Technical, is a millwright/ automotive engineer. His trucks are miniaturized versions of the latest commercial models. They have all the options, including working lights that we truly marvel at, come dusk. Each iteration comes with either of two bodies: a one third high stone or a full cane body. Anxious assistants who scurry to locate raw materials from which he hews the basic shapes surround him.

His penchant for quality workmanship heavily influences his selection of apprentices. Neither Ackee back of her hand directly beneath them, makes contact with the falling jacks then retards their motion in a cultured area at the convergence zone of her hand and fingers, slows them, as if with the reverse thrust of a jet engine, retaining as many as possible. Caught, they must be deftly tossed in the air in a reverse motion just high enough to be caught in the palm just prior to catching the ball after a single bounce. She then collects the inadvertently shed pebbles individually. Then she must spread them out singularly and collect them on the bounce in-group increments of one; the goal is to retrieve them all.

Jumping rope is also a favourite pastime of the girls, but rope is too expensive so we improvise with wild parasitic vines (wiss) torn from guango trees and stripped of their leaves. We must be careful for every time the vine touches a surface, it ejects sap that causes the skin to itch for several days; we suffer until the toxins are neutralized over time.

We listen to the cryptic tales; bathed in fear, to the story of the one-legged duppy mon who assumes a human form only to be revealed and cause a hasty, mass exodus. Dejected he calls: "Bam chickie yam hunnu wait fe me dey."

We tell other stories as well but always seem to end the night, with the most recent, scary duppy story.

In the welcoming glow of Tilley lamps on the piazzas of grocery shops we warm up with tales of Bere Annancy or Bere Rabbit. Sensing our fear others hide in the dark to scare us.

On moonshine nights, we share duppy stories; the effects are intensified by the phobia. The visual effects of swaying banana leaves, dew-laden branches and trees cause many of us to go home with our hearts in our mouths and our feet in our hands.

Teens and adults with the gift of gab sit around and spin the yarn. Those with "The Gift" swear blind to seeing Bagga's deceased sister, headless, but with trinkets around her neck, who hung her pregnant self rather than live with the shame of carrying parson's twin. She is seen wearing her white-laced frock walking swiftly, yet silently, across the mat of crisp, dried leaves covering the family's burial plot.

A cluster of bamboo trees hanging over the river rubbing against each other in a gentle breeze test the bladder control of the fearful homeward-bound. Jet —for his elusive speed when we play chevvy-chase—, petrified, tackles the dark road, to Killside. Alone. Tractor's parked truck is concealed in the pitch-blackness of the 'S' bend. Running home, he collides head first with the truck, pierces his scull, all that Jet recalls is waking up on the pavement, bathed in headlights. Night

-bus driver Gryah the Indian encounters him uncon-
scious, sprawled in the middle road, a gaping wound
an inch above his eyes in the dead centre of his forehead. At the co-pilot position, Mongoose is the second person to see him. He alights and runs up to Jet
balling out,

"'Sas C'ris' him mus ded, him mus de'd."
Mongoose carries him home. Jet's mother administers
first aid: sugar and water. Mongoose, "Boy listen to
you mother, drink the sugar and water."
He refuses.

"Keep him up Mongoose... me just spit into
this little grated bizzy... need it and put it pon the
cut."

"You mean like poultice mah!"
Mother: "Yes. Hold up you head! Me done yu go
sleep."

"Ow!"

"Thanks Mongoose."

Next morning at the clinic...

"Mawnin Nurse, tree mile me and me boy walk
Maam. Head buss. Beg you mek dakta see him no
Maam."

"All the people ahead of you did not come here
because they are healthy you know!"

"Yes nurse. Sorry nurse." She adds this while

265

admiring the disinfected floor. The doctor bills her for the dressing and bandages, throws in a guinea injection and sends them home. He's been called "Cyclops" ever since the bandages came off.

* * *

Good Friday, Mama stays in bed, eats no breakfast, calls us into her room and regurgitates the Easter story: "Celebrate the life of Jeezas.... Read here for me Sonny."

"Yes Mama."

"And no go too far, a need you every hour."

"Yes Maam."

The serious abstains from breakfast; the really serious also attend early service, and then chart His eight and two miles path from Pilot Hall to Calvary. We perform time-related experiments: at nine a.m., albumin from chicken's egg released into a big glass of water and left undisturbed in the sun's warmth. When the bus passes at eleven o'clock, the shape is interpreted. The consensus of the observers' dictates what the future holds for the practitioner: the shape of a ship or plane indicates travel; that of a foetus, a pregnancy; a ring, a wedding.... At noon we cut the Physic Nut tree. The usual white sap oozes from it blood red confirms His crucifixion. Mama remains in bed until after The Spirit leaves The Body, three o'clock, or more specifically, when three o'clock bus passes. Now she eats for the first time today, flatulence besieges her. Now the bun and cheese start to flow.

Easter Sunday service attracts all believers, incites them to raise triumphant songs like, "Up from the grave He arose." More bun an cheese and black pepper with fry fish.

Easter Monday's dawn brings true celebration to the masses. The a/c generator comes to life just outside the bamboo wattle dance hall, constructed for the occasion, for a day and night of ska. Maas Herby brings out his little leather cup, his three dices and his Crown and Anchor Board. Overturning a borrowed drum, he rattles his dices with markings of a crown, anchor, heart, spade, diamond and clubs we prefer to call bees-wing.

To draw the requisite betting participants he demonstrates his wrist skills and verbal repertoire to the onlookers: "Spot and beat the banker," his hand, fingers and little leather cup are an art form of gyrations. Upside down on the table, "Easy put on...easy take off," dices unexposed, he makes his final pitch, "No name no change," then raises the cup so that a tempted onlooker from his usually male-only crowd perceives himself as a winner.

Tonight he suffers the financial loss attributed

to the diversion and dice exposure tactics of a tag team from Kingston. He will not go home to Miss Ruby with much. And will start the week at the whim of the storekeeper who charges more for the water-soaked version of the codfish, watered down rum, and the watered down cooking oil which, the minute the emulsion gets hot above the guava wood, create its own 'hell n powder house.'

Come dusk, the underage must retreat from the sets festivities or face the wrath of their parents. Young adults intent on 'shaking a leg' must have been on their best behaviour to get the permission of their guardians. Once there, in the shadow-interrupted rays of the pulsating thirty-watt bulb, promises made to chiffon over taffeta and crinoline-wearing damsels are broken the moment the words are spoken.

Hours beat, dance in a full swing; a/c generator rhythm competes with Bob Marley "talkin' blues." Mongoose, imbibe a shot of Whites and lock down with Prinnell next to one of V Rocket's speakers. He is in her ear, his left hand in the small of her back locking their torsos in rhythmic cadence: "Yu no love me?" She nods.

Forty-fives being forty-fives times a going,
Homeboy's dissertation competition is expiring

the record, the disk jockey must remove
Because it's at the end of the groove

Yes remove that piece of musical wax
And install another from his stacks.
This is the normal mode of operation
And the entire population

That either frequents
Or lives close enough to such establishments
Are very much aware
Of the impending silence in the air

But for the staccato
Of the combustion engine electric generator
But Mongoose, due to the inspirational urgency
Brought on by a physical insurgency

Is on a whole other agenda
He is thinking: Oh she's soft an tenda
No need for additional focus of his emotion
He persists with the conversation.

The words of a slower, more suggestive song
Dance in his head tells him it won't be long:

269

"It's now or never, come hold me tight,
Kiss me my darling be mine tonight,

Tomorrow may be too late...."
He begins to contemplate
Under the influence his questioning persists.
But with the white Rum now ripe he insists

With a new urgency in his voice,
He shouts words of exquisite choice
They land comparatively softly on her eardrums,
Like the soft petals of chrysanthemums

"So yu naw mek we go..."
As the song ends yu dun kno...
What him say
And she feel like streggay

*   *   *

The singular deterrent to alcohol consumption is un-affordability. Seasoned, ceramic-like throats grant the potent substances, safe passage to rupturing stomach walls. Frequent ingestion bestows a badge of honour: "De Man him can really hol' 'im waters."

On weekends
They make amends

The walking dead
Need spirits in their head

Working dead-end jobs
They need to drown their sobs
Barely making two ends meet
They gather almost broke in the street

A few pennies short on the first shot
Everything else matters not
They show up at the bars
Waiting on passing men with cars

Show up on a day with a new name
A day with the same game

Beg yu a liquor baas
Buy me one sah yu look like a man wid class
He should know the first wouldn't be the las'
It's the lifestyle of the alkies in the poorer class

*   *   *

As an icebreaker, Butty Prince swiftly breaches
the culturally accepted interpersonal distance and strikes
with deadly breath, a pungent body odour and toothless
smile. A look of consternation creases the face of the
foreigner. Butty Prince is apologetic, "Sorry fe come

up into you face like that sar but me could have swear that you was Maas Such."

"Oh we all make mistakes sometimes."

"Dat is true… den yu is who sah?"

The Interloper: "Well my name is Josephus McKenzie and a come here to meet one Mr. Porter about some land…"

"Oh sar me know him, a me a firs' cousin, me bessis lickle cousin, me use to tek care of him from him yeye de a him knee! Any t'ing what him come off to him haffy t'ank me cause me used to help him cross river when it come down, car' him pon me back when de dutty watah did too deep. Yes sah. Yes sah. Den like how him nuh come yet we nuh can knock wan one drink sah?"

The man offering the drink is not financially bound to pay. Payment is expected from the philanthropic interloper. You stop in your car. You pay. Last week it was Mr. Richards. He was just passing through when he said to Butty Prince: "Oh, I'm going on to Mandeville and a just stop to stretch me legs."

His comeback: "Oh me know a which part. It is quite far. Such being the case den we nuh haffy knock a one before you leave out den bass, you need one fe de long journey."

"Knock one! I don't even drink!"

"Dat no say baas… me drink!"
When the Insurance Salesman C.L.U. --Clever Lover
Undercover-- stops by to check Miss Lou, Butty Prince
is right on spot: "From a she you a check right up
there-so and yu say yu and she a cuzzen, me hav fe
consider you fambily. Yes sah! You good as fambily
because me a fe Miss Lou firs cuzzen you know sah!"
The effect of his barrage affects the outcome.
The interloper: "So what you say we go into the bar
and have a drink?"

> The beggar's gastric juices gush
> one drink is all that's needed
> to induce the cerebral rush
> to start the ball rolling to stomachs eroded

> Get the waters flowing
> Hence
> All statements leaving
> on the interloper's lips a gospel pretence
> the beggars place him on a pedestal
> almost to the level of a being celestial

> Other hangers on inept at such
> persuasive introductions blush
> and along with the late arrivals converge
> in the doorway in a surge

273

The big pretence begins
The opening to such things
are beggars standardized performances
reusing statements and sentences
some overused soliloquy of the misrepresenting
guardian of the status quo
our local politrickal appointee
he opines with a bit of local eloquence
gets his whistle whet

It also whets those of the cling-ons
Garnering the gulp the gullible
galled at their adult grief give in to
guilt-ridden submergence options consciences
crave in order to forget their plights
from the cradle to the grave

Hungry
mouths at home to feed
minor misusings
misusing minors
uses and abuses of the suppressed kind

They hope the quick gulps of the substance
will offer respite from the plight
the fright

if only for a day turned night
by the shot of white
Rum

All throats enter a clearing contest. Trivial mumbles and cynical grins are pallet-preparation in exuberance. To the philanthropist, it's only pennies. But it's still too rich for the blood of the self-deceiving exploit artist and his cronies. The philanthropist can ill afford to be a sucker for every illiterate, barefooted, two bit pie in the sky, pregnant with faith, living in hope, charity expecting con man lurking in some gas station deprived bushtropolis or he'll eventually join them. But to verbally isolate and deny a sufferer is asking for trouble. The adept at such pleadings attaining this reputation show great tenacity in extending their emporium stays. Butty Prince: "Then yu play domino sar?"

"Yes! Well I am not too bad actually…"

"Den mek we lick a six before yu leave no sar?" The philanthropist's identification of the alpha male is key. But still, on this day at Ackee Red's rum bar; Auntie Missis, Driver, Jacket Beloved, Perkle, Pilgrim, Poorer, Richman and Whiteman, close in. Silent bedlam emanates beyond the doorway; glance their way and be greeted with natural dental jobs gone bad. With any lull in the drinking, the bartender sends his coded message: "Butty Prince, how you sound so hoarse? Throat a get dry man…"

Attain these liquor-drinkin heights, because of poorly managed lifestyles, and doctor may warn: "Curb the habit!" Such warnings make it back to the district formulated as: "Him get a 'trong warning from Dackta." All along, there are private indicators unobserved by his compadres and kept away from immediate family. His increasingly frequent and unseen vomiting of blood, acid reflux and hypersensitivity to even mildly spicy foods begin to concern him. The happiness abounding in the killer white rum creates an addict way beyond any ego trip. The addiction becomes a leash. Again, dragged to the Doctor's office and cautioned: "You going to kill y'uself if yu don't stop drink so-so white rum" opens his eyes briefly. But the firewater clouds his reasoning.

Still Butty Prince and his kind present real problems to our society, themselves, their families and the impressionable young men they corrupt. Because Butty spends his waking moments and last penny maintaining unwanted notoriety, he gets accolades for being an Alkie. His unique drenching style becomes a death-chasing signature. He is foolishly respected. Put on a pedestal. His problem-curbing inability elevates him to cult status: "He is a rummer! A man that can hol' him waters!" By the stroke of poverty, many of these men come into this earth, born walkin' and dead pedestrian. Hasten his visit to the ultimate cult emporium. Such a warning goes unheeded by the stiff's compadres. They perpetuate the lifestyle beginning with the days between his death and funeral. Gather at the dead yard twenty-four seven and consume more of the same. Premature gullets, unsuited for the rum, choose Beer, Stout and Milk Stout as their poison. Fortunately for the alcohol-induced poverty stricken, related loved ones left behind, forced into premature mourning by a product and psyche, the district kicks in and contributes food, fellowship, funeral planning and funeral expenses. For the days leading up to the burial, the fireside is hardly without a stoked fire. Foodstuff and large pots appear. Livestock is slaughtered and the family of most of his drinking buddies as well as those knowing his usually church-going spouse --common-law or otherwise-- contribute their time, energy and portions of their savings to 'save face' and put him away as respectably as possible.

Naturally, parson seizes the opportunity to caution one and all about the fragility of souls and our ability to punch holes in the pretty pictures the Devil paints to coax us into joining him.

*   *   *

Terrence R. E. Burey

Back with Mr. Richards
in his district of Bellas Gate
those affording to state
with only a smile contemplate
those with prosperous wishes
and kind words
reap wonderful rewards
every time he goes
home.

Today's picture
of prosperity
was in rags
of a common variety
yesterday
with stains,
holes,
rips,
patches
and vestiges
of original colours.

Unlike the way he was
he returns
GQ'd to the max
chash and ready

in a pair of popular booty
on yesterday's
bare-pavement-rippers.

Former ill wishers
brow-beaters
and downpressors
in a state of gaiety
fictitiously
recall
being well-wishers,
affectionate,
generous,
attentive,
understanding,
and loyal caregivers
and proceed
to beg money,
a drink,
or both.

With
an elephantine memory
and an alerting wink,
fake souls get updated
on their forgetfulness;

graphically:

"Yu
'membah when yu use to run me?
Go look work!
Go look sitten fe teef!
You no membah?
But me no fegat.

Come out a me face."

Chapter Sixteen

BY NOVEMBER, HARVEST, AS A RESULT OF the previous emancipation day festivities and the long summer break from school, nuff ban belly start to show and them girls realize that a nuh something whe' a go a something whe a come. All young people as well as the young at heart converge on the fair in schoolyard, which has attractions that include a donkey ride, maypole dancing and a merry-go-round. It's at the heart of the harvest that the oranges are the sweetest but my friends and I suffer earlier as well as later citrus toxicity when we 'go juice.' With a ginger knife or two and

Mongoose's loaner 'ratchet', we select trees and consume enough juice to swim in. Three dozens is a good number per individual but piles of peels and refuse are better indicators. Full, we engage in ego-bruising quarrels over quantitative analyses. Regression theories abound, recalling who is on the fifth when who is on first, all kind of horse dead and cow fat. Labrish. All kind of cock and bull story. At the end of the game we can hardly walk. Oh, Watchie can curtail such actions so it's in our best interest to keep it down. Not the juice, the noise. In time, Watchie progresses from being just a verbal threat of a man with two long hands, to a 'bu's' me' whipping stick, to his sword machete, to his dawg --his irons. His gun provides all the incentive we need to remember the proverb "Silence is golden." We keep this in mind before Watchie start burs' carbine.

*   *   *

Commercials bombard the airwaves with Christmus pipe dreams describing the available but unaffordable happenings and trappings. Just about every working adult gets a bonus from the last ratoon ginger, pimento or chocolate crop. Some buy a little whitewash and with a coconut tree's fruit support stem beaten into a faux paintbrush, apply it to the stones along pathways to hither and yon and on the low portion of every tree's trunk with a chance of being viewed from the road. Pickneys' unable to bum a penny from parents or guardians sell bottles and buy starlights to be a part of the after dark, ground bound meteor show. An obstinate Jackass points out that the world is not level: In local shops, hanging displays with numbered, disproportionately sized balloons compete for our pennies. To win, one buys a ticket, submerge it in water, set it on the counter and watch the litmus test as the lucky number becomes visible after a brief reaction. These balloons provide brief wholesome joy then burst into smithereens, which is not the end of our fun; we grab the scattered pieces, which provide fun for the junior masses and entertain nearly the whole district. Stretching a piece over the tip of one's little finger then placing that finger in one's mouth and sucking real hard on the fragment, inhale some air around the finger, and create a mini balloon the size of a marble. Pinching the end real tight, then twisting it creates a spirally wound tight seal which becomes a blissful chi-ki-chi-ki.

When we do this simultaneously, it's common to have adults ask us to vamoose with the noise because "Their ears can't eat grass." Herein lies the evidence that it's the ears that first became vegetarian. For the icing on our Christmas

Missa Venroy's film show is a mus
His movies on the silver screen

With sticks local sword fighters are seen
Cutting each other to smithereens

We fight to follow the dialogue
From prologue to epilogue
Contrary to any Christmas carol's description
One horse open sleigh
Jackass saddle…. Yea
Silent night, holy night
V Rocket a revellers delight
Pretty sidewalk --irregular embankments
The midnight clear --moonshine night
Oh little star of Bethlehem --satellite
Rudolph the red-nosed reindeer
Atop his motorcar an assistant at the steer
At high noon on Grand Market day
No soft shoulder for us to lay
In wait, no silent night or day
He rides in a cloud of dust
A metal speaker P.A. system his presence thrust
He rolls through town atop his open sleigh
Jettison one-pound paper bags every which way
The fastest sprinters gather most of his gifts
Fee-fee, balloons, rattles, candy canes they lift
White dolly babies,
jax sets and star lites we collect and exchange

At barter time nothing is off limits
including fights
We compete for the highest blasting milk can
Again deciding the biggest and baddest man
Burs chi-bum at the feet of those turned away
Light firecrackers while we are feeling gay
Back in the day
When all it meant was healthy play
Can't wait for the darkness to light the star lights
Off bottle lights
Older and more daring boys make gas balloons
Using silver paper and acid like a crazy goons
One has to remain quite alert
As many a mischievous little squirt
Gun at the string to release in the breeze
Balloon heavenbound the owner ill at ease
Girls not yet caught up in the puberty thing
Join us and we all have a good fling

It's the only time of year that most kids enjoy their childhood. All get an opportunity to play with anything other than the toys nature provides; leaf race in the river, Yard style bobsledding on coconut boughs, baseball with lime ball and bamboo bat, Indian with bamboo and English cord bows and bamboo arrows, cricket with bamboo bat and bamboo root ball. Penned letters may work for some adult demands but poor children bark up the wrong tree by sending to ask a ghetto dweller with address ending in letters or half numbers such as 2A, 2B, 2C or 151/2 Matches Lane or 278 3/4 Spanish Town Road, in Kingston to forego food and send fee fee. Fe who? Dem mad as shad.

* * *

The bamboo plant also produces, in single large sections, flotation devices; banded sections make rafts, split sixteen ways and exploded on one end this conical shape combined with a two square-foot piece of chicken wire to make a fish trap; split eight ways it wattles structures to form: from temporary dance halls to kitchens to the residences, when mixed with mud daubed over its exterior; dried it becomes firewood with accelerant qualities that must be monitored as it can reduce buildings to smoke and ashes lickety split. It wicked bad.

* * *

No one's seen Primrose since the belly start show. Homebound midway through her final year of parochial school, she schedules her activity external to the house to coincide with dusk or later. She's moving sluggishly and there is no one to push her. Mother and sister left this morning to Christiana to sell the chocolate, dried, parched, chummed and rolled along with grater cake, drops and sweet potato pudding. Grand market night Miss Birdie's wire clothesline, formerly attached to the side of the outdoor kitchen is left hanging, so to speak, when the bamboo sided, thatched roof kitchen erupts in flames. It sure put a damper on the festivities. Grand Market is usually Christmas Eve but because Christmas falls on a Monday this year, the marketing is actually done on Saturday and we go to Church on Sunday and again on Christmas Day. The island's Spanish name "Xayamica" translates to "Land of wood and water" but fires are a lot more prevalent that floods. Abundant lumber: Cedar, Guango, Mahogany and Mahoe trees and for thatched roofs the Coconut palm fronds, ante up their fuels to keep us in a state of fire preparedness. So whenever a catastrophe of this kind rears its head, the local citizenry makes it their civic responsibility to get together and save each other.

Primrose through her non-compliance with the code of ethics: "Yu gwaan 'tan'up, 'tan'up out a' roadside a chat up chat up with dem bwoy and see wha' goin' to happen to you." The sex education course: "'F a ketch yu with man a kill yu." Or the catchalls; "Wha' sweet yu it wi' soon sour yu." "And watch what you get at night for sure as day follow night it will come to light." Ended up sprigment. With all that forewarning she, as it turned out, was improperly forewarned, thus improperly forearmed about the sweet mout' b'woys.

After privately getting over the morning sickness, she starts her chores: collects and washes all the lambs breath and plastic roses with a little soap powder in the face basin, hangs them upside down on the clothesline, then, after a little break for lunch consisting of brebbage and crackers, she gets cracking on the white washing of walls and tree roots with temper lime, using beaten banana stalks. She hangs the late arrival Christmas cards Royal Mail brought yesterday and today on the cord draped on the most conspicuous side of the living room.

She dusts the bureau in her mother's room, then the one in her sisters' room, saving her rickety three-legged beauty for last; she cleans the floor with the commonly used straw dye and bees wax while humming, "Have Thine own way Lord," she knocks Johnny Cuppa, "Thou Art Tha Potter I am the clay." She wipes on some elderberry straw dye on another small area, passes the beeswax over the kitchen bitch to melt a little and strokes the coconut brush with it so as to add polyurethane-like protection to the mirror-like sheen. "Make me and mould me after Thy will…" the thought crosses her mind; even though the baby is illegitimate she'll ask just the same special wish for it.

Next she sweeps the pathway bordered by whitewashed river stones with flanking Ginger Lilies on the right and a multicolour Rose Garden on its left, all the way to the rivers edge then bathes in the bath-pan beside the kitchen. She cleans the lampshades and fills the lamps with oil. She's lit all but hers when the mangy dog Rover started a friendly barking.

They return from market and have dinner that has gone cold but cannot be heated because the wood-fire is dead. After dinner, her mother takes a bath under the cellar in the big bath pan. Her sister at the south end of Long Water takes hers quietly. No one passing by on the road just above is any wiser.

Primrose enters her dark room with sleep on her mind and fumblingly locates the matches on the little bedside table, next to the exposed wall stud. Ambidextrously caressing the air, she expertly locates both the shade and the lamp. She lays the shade on the bed, strikes a match and lights the lamp. The sudden kick startles her. The kick is the first from her unborn child. Uneducated, inexperienced and oblivious to all else, she instinctively reaches for her stomach, fingers on both hands spread as if catching something. The matchstick lands on the bed, makes quick work of the four-count bed linen and a small section of the coir. She holds it, trying to curtail what she imagines to be an attempt at premature and improper uterine escape, then it kicks again, a lingering trailing kick and she smiles; the second kick instinctively reassuring her, she is happy. Happiness she can only share with her sister, not her mother. Perhaps the result of pain above the threshold, the brain issues a "Don't care" to the feeling nerve. Sitting on her bed with a sigh of relief, she firstly becomes keen to the scent of roasting flesh then sharp pain to her heinie, which almost causes her to hit the roof. She bawl out, "Lard a Massey me bu'n up me batty!" Her reflex action to the battie singe is to jump out of bed. As she does, she bumps the shaky three-legged bedside table, kin-catting the lamp, ricocheting it, flame first, between the sheet and the table onto the floor. The relatively slow rate of descent keeps the flame alive; the spilling kerosene spreads across the floor, ignites and races up the flimsy sheet to the coir mattress. For her sake, the flames do not need the spilled kerosene, as the available oxygen is adequate fuel. As it races through a section of the coir mattress and bed linen alike, Primrose runs and bawl out, "Fire!" And rush back with the tablecloth and try to snuff out the blaze. But it backfires and works as a fan instead. The flames quickly overcome her and before you can say "who dat" they engulf Miss Nicey's house side.

Both women curtail their baths hurriedly. The soapy bath water under the cellar is quickly transformed into flame retardant, scum and all. Babsy makes a dash into her room to save some belongings she's convinced she can't live without and to prove it, she wears the scars on the left side of her face and the underside of her right hand for life.

On hearing someone bellow "Fire," each person within earshot yell's 'fire', grabs a portable container then dashes in the direction of the sound. Districtites make this a flawless response. A human chain from the embankment to the house forms quickly: in communicative unison, "Empty, full, pan, bucket, ketch it, got it, come to me, come to me."

Built to survive all but the worst floods, the house on stilts now quickly evapourates the water that's clinging to its embers. The chain meanders through the drawing room to the rear bedroom. Flames attach to the sides in a swift-consuming cadence, reaching ever onward and ever upward. The fire brigade is no match for the fuel. The cataclysmic cadence continues until there was no more fuel.

They're penniless, possessionless and homeless.

Daylight, on Sunday morning, removes the evidence of burning embers, leaves only trailing smoke and a pile of ashes at the end of the walkway of cris whitewash trees and stones. From a distant radio, a Chris'mus carol reminds of the season. The women gather by the side of the road to discuss the calamity. Overnight, different versions vie for credibility. Incredulous. Miss Blanche: "God naw sleep! Him a punish Miss Nicey. She badmouth Sister Sweetie, say she no have no control over her gal pickney dem. Regardless, the two of them get pregnant at the same dance in a August, she no have no business fe say what she say."

Miss Dawkers answers: "A swift God retribution dat."

"Miss Nicey surely gwine to put har husban' luv to de tes' for she need plenty money fe rebuild." Miss Blanche: "Him de with w'ite humman a Hinglan to get him papers straight an' can't sen' all de money come gi'e har right inna de Chris'mus 'cause dem mus' wan' fe live lickle life to."

Mout' a Massey Miss Lizah chimes in: "Ev'ry ting epsep what them have on 'pon dem back bu'n up so all dat plus baby clothes money him haffy sen come."

Miss Gattie: "An' Mam me got it fram good source sey dat dem humman, especially de Hinglan one dem, wan' fe tek over de man dem heart, soul and pocket."

Miss Dawkers: "An' Maam me got it from good source say dem bad! Fe me lickle half a foot one him siddung up a yard de now tired like a dawg. Gaa wo'k from

Gad sen' marnin chack back till Gad sen' night. De little pittance dat dem gi'e him a pay-bill so him can carry it home fe come do jus' dat. Pay bill. Bill up a top shop. Bill a Miss Merty. Bill down a' Maas Taa't. Bill a Drivah. Bill a Ackee Red. Be time we dun pay bill, eh eh, wha' me a sey, befo'e we dun pay bill de little pittance done."

*   *   *

Christmas celebrations go on, Denominational cantatas rule. Local, semi-literate actors and actresses are showered with accolades with their delivery of Baba-like mispronounced words. Equally illiterate neighbours cough up monies into the collection plate to "put up" one actress in encore and "take down" another for poor performance.

On Boxing Day, the day after Christmas, the staunchest Christians conveniently miss the flyers on the telegram posts and on the sides of the shops next to signs declaring, "Paste no Bills" inform of the impending dance. Anticipating the shindig, the youth, teens and twenty-something's put a freeze on the collection plate and donation cards. The electricity in the air as well as the electricity generating units works with the music, work as shake a leg advertisement to the illiterate and uninformed. Maas Herby comes out with his little leather cup, three dice and Ludu Board.

Come nightfall the single light bulb suspended from the diagonally strung wire, pulse to the a/c, while those forking over the night-time cover charge pulse to the direct current, turntable rhythms in the dancehall where nuff rum, milk stout, beer and Dandy Shandy a flow.

* * *

The New Testament Church of God is an incomplete Spiritual sentinel as a result of Parson Timon runnin' out of money. Cellarless, windowless, naked doorways, unevenly hardened clay floor with pastor's pulpit on a higher mound, the congregation gets good practice 'walking the literal' straight and narrow. In Spirit, all sanctimonious, jumping and getting jiggy with it, the congregation bounces on the irregular floor. Their tag-along offsprings are particular objects of ridicule, jokes and inquisitions by their peers:

"A wha' language yu madda chop last night?"

"Hey, girl, your madda is a German mek she talk so?"

"Oh raaee toe taw, a wha' kin' a labrish that missis?"

"You madda mus' be a foreign diplomat."

The fusillade of snide comments produce kids with heads permanently hung low, low on self esteem, low on pride, a permanently embarrassed bunch.

Chapter Seventeen

MAMA AND I TRAVEL EAST IN EARLY summer. We visit Dahlia and family in Port Maria. We visit Aunt Petal, she is proud of my progress. I spend the latter part of the summer with my mother in Essex Hall. The houses are perched on uneven but horizontally equal stilts along the steeply descending sides of the Mountain Range that runs through the heart of the burg. The narrow road meanders along its apex and the taxi driver daring enough to venture here must be skilled at backing as there is absolutely no safe place to turn.

* * *

Our leaders organize a boom-shack-a-lacka Independence following negotiations in which the colonial rulers lose the stranglehold and lower The Union Jack so that we can raise the yellow, green and black. We gain our Independence on August 6, 1962; we choose our National Anthem and motto, "Out of many one people" perhaps a more apt would be, "One big Rock One Melting Pot."

During June and July, parishes pick a Farm Queen. Now all roads lead to Denbeigh where, in one big splash, we choose The Island Queen, cow, hog and dog, pumpkin, onion, tomato, escallion and garlic. We come by chartered buses and trucks; trains, drays and walk for days along trails. On the first day of festivities the intense summer heat causes 'fish to suffer jock itch.' With a wet second day, the pigs get all jiggy in the mud. While the girls salvage their pedal pushers boys save their light-grey stripe gun-mout' pants. We both rescue our best pair of shoes and bosonova shirts. Men get drunk, some on stagger-back stagger back; young and old, unable to figure out a terrain without hills and gullies, yam sticks and cane fields get lost. Some get lucky on different fronts, including winning dunzi from the three-card man and at the crown and anchor table or bawlin' for more as everybody juggle on the dance floor dropping legs to the sounds of V Rocket, King Tubby's and King Jammy's Hi Fi as they repeatedly play Toots and the Maytals, Sweet and Dandy, the festival song.

*   *   *

It's the end of summer break and I'm confused as to why I must move from this one where I see Mama and Dada every day.... Isn't it a similar classroom? So begins my contribution to an island-wide epidemic, schlepping all over creation, in the name of education! Going for the milk, mama reminds me to bid farewell to Bredda Chris and Aunt Duncie. After breakfast I'm walking around and telling everybody goodbye. Leaving some homes, I am asked to wait; hands reach into pockets, some into bosoms; thread bags get unknotted and I get 'a smalls'. Paying me to leave? I wonder briefly, then take comfort in the fact that I can buy stuff en route: Sweetie, bulla cake, drops, gizzada, peanuts, grape nut ice cream, patty, bun an' cheese and cola champagne.

Saturday I leave home. Sad. Loneliness sets in as I set foot on the bus. The normally melodious, harmonally stimulating engine sparks no excitement. I cry off and on all the way to the terminus in Christiana and on the second bus as well. The sudden salvation among the passengers which precedes the bend from hell erases all the traces of tears. Smukums greets me when I alight and senses my depression. She reminds me that the sea is nearby. Suddenly I'm proud to be a swimmer and I share animated details of how I learned to swim. To welcome me 'home', the minister pats my back so hard it feels like a spanking. In a lengthy supplication he thanks The Heavenly Father for protecting me on the long and dangerous journey where so much could have gone wrong were it not for His Mighty Hands. I eat a late dinner. Assigned to a cot and a couple bureau drawers, I make myself comfortable and retire as we will rise early in the morning for prayer, breakfast and a day of worship. Having just prayed on arrival and again when I had dinner, I climb into bed and Auntie quickly advises I that I forgot to pray. My knees hit the floor before she can say another word. Pity my simplicity...

I'm added to the duty roster. Tiny is the youngest and the only non-relative here. She has the milk run in the mornings and watergrass hunt for the rabbits, by the lake after dinner. The chores are now jointly ours. Eleven years old, Tiny 'roots bad', we get along just fine. No amount of ramrodding religion down Tiny's throat denies her tendency to chart her own course. Part of that course includes sexual promiscuity. Smukums suspects. It's Tiny's idea that we feign displeasure at having to accompany each other to get the watergrass, but when we are sent to do it, we fail to hide our enthusiasm. Smukums shows up one evening, instead of pulling grass.... Reported, we get our first beating at the hands of Brother G. The second: The Sunday we come home before communion to light the in-house, wood burning stove and decide to simultaneously light our own... Smukums exits Church, takes the long way home, enters quietly through the front gate and silently through the front door and catch us again.

The excitement takes a backseat; I'm really missing home now. The dinner bell rings and drags me out of a homesick trance; we all sit down to eat. Brother G asks that we bow our heads and close our eyes and almost causes the dinner to go cold before he finishes thanking Him again for sparing us to be together again and also that He cleanse the evil minds of those seated who choose fornication over supplication. He prays so hard for the deprived and those not having a meal this evening that guilt starts to rest on my conscience to the point where I want to go walk the streets and find someone hungry and give him or her mine. I'm not that big on eating. Especially tonight. I fall asleep sobbing, missing Mama, Dada and the crew. In what seems like the next moment, I'm awake and with matter in my eyes digesting instructions to meet in the living room for Morning Prayer. We randomly select "Daily Word" cards, read them aloud and following protocol, give my quattie inference on the card I pick. Baba Laiza, I need you. It did not take long for everyone else to realize what I already knew; I had spent more time on academics and at play. Not enough on religion to cut the mustard here. Brother G bristles at my religious deficiency. His ever-shifting eyes seem to target everything simultaneously. My first experience at lacking enough religious awareness to be alive here comes at me through the crash of his palm on my thinly protected buttocks as I kneel for prayer. He wonders aloud: "What in the world could cause a child like you, related to my wife, to be so spiritually deficient in these, the last days." Apparently, he is trying to instigate religious osmosis. Two weeks into the program my spiritual education stimulant, his guava whip, a.k.a. rod of correction, attempts direct injection of spiritual trivia by burning into my buttocks every word he burns into my ears. Living a' parson yard I quickly learn to walk the walk and talk the talk. When I write Mama, Aunty deems it necessary to read same before the mailing. She suggests rewrites, omitting the "I miss you and want to come home." This is the beginning of my

YOUTMAN   Saturday's Child

shifting home base between my vacational and vocational places of residence. Home! Where's home?

School starts and Auntie goes into drill sergeant mode; my right knuckles pay the price as she spanks me on them with the bamboo ruler. Ensures that I form letters properly, filling the spaces in my double lines, exercise books. "All your relatives have lovely penmanship... you are not going to be an exception," she constantly reminds. This probably, indirectly has something to do with why, even among the enlightened and exposed family members, so few are doctors. But Dada's domestic and world geography lessons are paying huge dividends; I am ranked high on my teacher's list as one of the bright sparks. This information is not lost on the principal, who, in teaching sixth class, the uppermost in the upper school, calls me from time to time to answer questions, which have stumped his class. The principal explains: "I have asked certain geographical questions of these boys and they can't answer me. I told them you could. If I'm wrong in my assessment then I'll spank you, but if you know the answer then they will get it. Do I make myself clear?"

"Yes teecha."

He asks. I answer. I'm right. In one sentence he dismisses me and calls the first recipient. He spanks them for letting a little runt know more than he does. I proudly return to my class.

Then it's recess. While playing with my peers, the group suddenly thins the way a flock or school of prey does when a predator approaches. I'm boxed in, blows are being administered with warnings: "Anytime you come back and answer more question we going to gi'e you double the amount of wha' we get."

I test the accuracy of the statement the next week; they are correct. In two two's I decide that it's best not to answer the questions as such a ploy would eliminate the punches, which are probably worse than teecha beating. Headmaster will have none of it. As if he had taught me himself and therefore knows what's in my head, he beats me whenever I fail to answer correctly. I am damned if I do and damned if I don't. On the next occasion I answer his question.

The playing field is obscured from the principal's classroom and office. During recess following my latest, upper school visit, he visits it. My abusers are caught red-handed, whipped and promised more if the abuse recurs. If looks could kill, I'd be a dead man.

Auntie, at forty-one, has given over the idea of becoming a mother and treats me like her own son. Her husband, however, is different; frustrated, disappointed and jealous, he thrashes my 'hut' for whatever he perceives as a sin. When he sends me on errands, I must run to and fro, lest, in the eyes of The Lord, I took too much time. From The Good Book he takes as his mantra, "Spare the rod and spoil the child." And even though he is never sure when Tiny and I are up to anything, he sometimes just thrashes our huts on principle. Home from school this evening, my eldest cousin Mercy, tells me to clean out the Rabbit cage; my first time and I'm displeased. I learn a new word today and I let slip under my breath: "The reason you a single me out to do this a because you pregnant." I overhear the word pregnant when Auntie shares her unofficial new condition with her best friend, fellow teacher Miss Wallace. Having no idea what it means, I seize a dictionary: being with young. Yea this really helps. Paedophile, hanging out in the company of those outside your age group; that's me! I am absolutely clueless as to what it means. Had she said, "push down bread-van" I'd have had no trouble. Mercy does nothing but turn me in to Brother G. Auntie realises that most of the unnecessary murderations I receive are due to his childless frustration. This time she observes him administering the half killing, laying me across his lap and paraphrasing, by his standards, sinfully unrepeatable statements, then come down real hard across the same spot on my buttocks with his supple guava whip, Rapture, and in very halting speech says, "Youtman."

Then awaits a response: "Yes Bredda G."

"Why, why you tell Mercy that she pregnant?" Whap. The sucker soaks through to my thighs.

"Youtman."

"Yes Bredda G."

"Why, why you, why you tell Mercy she pregnant?"

"Nutten Bredda G." Whap, the sucker soaks deeper.

"Youtman."

"Yes Bredda G."

"Why, why you tell Mercy that she pregnant?"

"Nutten Bredda G." Whap.

My leg and his get warm with the compliments of my kidney's release. Sick, he keeps on. Six of these, all in the exact spot, same ferocity.

I'd hope to God that I have dinner before these occurrences as there is no way in hell to sit and eat anytime soon after. Regardless of the state of affairs on my backside though, if the dinner bell rings then, even if it means growing a new buttocks I'd better be seated at the table, say grace with everyone, and eat up like nothing happened. Transitioning from pet-lamb with Mama and Dada to Frustration's whipping boy is quite dramatic. Auntie has her fill of the brutality. As she arrives home from school she catches the tail end of a directive sending me to get Rapture. Auntie, without skipping a beat asks loud enough for him to hear.

"A whey de ly bwoy do now?"

"He misbehaved again, in the eyes of The Lord."

She pulls the classroom strap from her handbag and spread her legs until her blue Terylene and Wool skirt is taut across her thighs; holding me off to the left she uses her right hand to administer some serious sounding blows across the hollow part of the front of her skirt, whap, whap, whap, mid-strokes she leans her head over closer to my ear and softly says, "Bawl bwoy," whap, whap, whap, whap; saving my rump from certain torment.

*   *   *

I alight from the bus in front of the tailor shop and after the bear hug that takes my breath away; Mama sets me back on the ground. I greet Dada excitedly and he too is overjoyed to see me. They want to know,

"How are you getting along?"

"How's school?"

"Do you miss we sonny?"

"Guess who keep asking for you?"

"Did your father come to see you?"

"Did you go to the sea?"

"Be careful when you go sharks in the water!"
All before I can set my grip down. I rush downstairs to greet my friends Canepiece Rat and Ackee Red, refit into the old clique so naturally it seems I hadn't left. Back from the trampoose with my friends, Mama's only interest is to ensure that I write Auntie and let her know I reached home safely.

"Play with your friends... but write it today, today."

"Yes Mama, I wi do it today, we post it tomorrow."

"So it's just like old times eh." I say to Canepiece-Rat and Ackee Red.
Ackee Red, "Man mek we find sum ting different to do."
I use my new accent on my friends: "Me de tell hunnu dis inna secret; One ly gal live a de house an ebry day when we de look grass fe de ly rabbit dem...me an him...." They are amazed and listen intently... I continue..."De ly time de bus spen a Spaulin me de tell yu me go check Dimples and a jus because de layover so short...."
Ackee Red: "Whey yu would a do?"

"How you mean?"

"Yu Gadmadda neva deh deh?"

"Yea… so wha?"

"Yu a gallang like yu too bad yu couldn do nutten."

"A so yu tink!"

It's time to start wearing briefs.

Before too long we are on a full-time girl hunt. We extend the self imposed trampoosing boundaries in which we used to hoist kites, shoot birds, play statue, marbles, bathe in the river and look girls. I try the life and death line on Miss hard-to-get, Guava-Jelly: "Doctor tell me granny say if me don't get some of the thing me going to die." It works. I tell Canepiece Rat and Ackee Red. We actively make more cases with the life and death reason. Our girls are not old enough to 'have their sister visit from Red Hills'; no risk of the consequential damage; baby.

We want to do something different. To bond. We decide to head west with some guaranteed fish catching weapons: a bucket; few butter pans; couple machetes; a pound of rice, flour, a little cooking oil, kerosene oil and matches and newspaper to start the fire. People from near and far must come here, so we'll have to find a portion where we won't disrupt them. We head west thinking that locating a few jubbies wouldn't hurt either.

We come across four jubbies doing their family laundries and per the pig's adage: the first water hog comes to him wash; we stop. And boy it is a good thing that we do. We hit the mother lode. We make small talk to which they are receptive. Before long, humanistic sparks pair us up plus one. Washday is usually an all-day affair and so the group has already started a fire. They plan to cook lunch. Small talk between Canepiece-Rat and Daphnie confirms our date for next Tuesday even before we sort out today. Jenny and Grethel are reticent, but seeing the sparks between Daphnie and Canepiece-Rat, Ackee Red and I synergistically confirm that we better make inroads because the situation too nice to pass up.

Ackee Red: "A Gad sen hunnu, we leave home to stop water and catch all the fish and run a boat yu know!"

Daphnie: "Yes." Lots of giggles.

Ackee Red: "An' yu know wha! Not one o we can cook."

Jenny: "Me no think hunnu can even catch fish, but a promise you that if hunnu catch them we will cook them."

Canepiece-Rat breaks the silence: "So we can take the silence to mean consent then! That you will help us?"

That gets a few words out of Grethel: "We look hungry?"

Her other friends crack up. I see this as my opening: "No, you don't seem hungry… we are doing this for fun."

"I see."

"So Miss 'I see' do you have a name?"

"Yes."

Moving a little closer, but cautiously staying outside her space I add: "Is that what they call you 'Yes,' that's new."

"No, 'Yes' is not my name."

"Oh, really… I believed you there for a minute."

"Well that's not it."

"We are quite a ways up river anything is possible!"

"What are you talking about," she says this with a lovely smile. "Aye eye I. I must be getting somewhere."

"They charge by the words up this way? Talk about mincing words. You're really pinching them. Hey Ackee Red, we found a group of chatterboxes didn't we?"

"Boy tell me 'bout it?"

"I know I heard someone say a few words earlier; this one here, who are you lovely lady?"

"Jenny."

"Boy me get the wrong impression of these ladies."

"Boy me try a few of me bess lines yu know."

"Girls, excuse him for a minute. Come here?"

"Sure."

He comes over, "De gal dem no like the patois jus' speak de lingua and watch wha' happen."

"You notice that when I spoke she talked back?" Hear Ackee Red: "Boy I don't know what's the matter, I tried some of my better lines on you but none worked. But I always have a few more in the bag."

"Well tell them don't tell me!"

I return to Jenny: "I beg you pardon, where were we?"

"You were saying how I pinch my words like you're from somewhere else."

I talk on and when I mention that I'm away in school and only home for the holidays her eyes light up. I find the right button. The idea of a travelling man… or a studying man… I'll take either…

"So how far away is it?"

"It's over on the north coast."

"So you are near the sea."

"Yes, it's less than five minutes walk…"

"Do you go there often?"

"As often as I can."

"Is it ever rough?"

"Once you climb the hill, you can see it."

"That doesn't answer my question"

"I wasn't finished…"

"Oh."

"This way if it is choppy we can decide whether we want to continue."

"Who is we?"

"My cousins…"

"Anybody else?"

I suffer selective amnesia about Tiny: "There are fishermen that live in the district."

"So what's the name of the beach?"

"The people in the area call it Charity Hill."

"I've never been to the ocean."

"Don't let me stop you from washing."

"Why?"

"Even though that would leave just the two of us here, I don't think that would be fair."

"That's very nice of you, that's considerate."

"Well I have a feeling I'll be seeing enough of you, no need to stop you from doing your work."

"So you go to the beach a lot?"

"You never even ask me if I can swim?"

"It's obvious that you can swim!"

"And how so may I ask?"

"Non-swimmers never stand with their backs to deep water like you are."

"Smart too."

"I'd like to be smarter…"

"Are you uncomfortable with me watching you?"

"You're not uncomfortable watching me are you?"

"Hhmm, spunky!"

Canepiece-Rat is fishing for shrimp. Shrimp loves the taste of the soapy water and will extend themselves a little beyond the safety of their rock sanctuaries to absorb some. To girls cooking by the side of the river, there is hardly a better aphrodisiac. Boys willing to risk damage to their fingers as these crustaceans punch holes in their fingers with their vice-like claws which will also remove pieces of flesh if they don't clasp it just right, deserve every inch of whatever they get. Me, I'm betting on the power of words. I'm not putting my fingers in that kind of jeopardy. I go downstream of the girls' washing and stay close to the embankment with most of the soapy water, walk very slowly and keep my eyes peeled. I really don't focus on any one point in fact; I keep my eyes in a roaming mode looking for any movement. Once the shrimp sees me coming, it will quickly back into its hole and that's what I am looking for. Movement. I assess the rock it goes under and hope it's not one that weighs more than a stone. If it isn't then, I'll lift it slowly so the sudden currents or exposure to light won't startle it. Now having it in an exposed corner, I can slowly move in, God help me if it's a male; having it focusing on one hand, I'll grasp it across the back with the other. It's even possible to catch a crayfish on occasion, but as its right claw is a lot bigger I definitely leave those to the experts.

"So how long are you going to be away at school?"

"Oh I don't know; my Aunt teaches there."

"Is it helping you?"

"I suppose so."

"How's that?"

"She insists that I study."

"Are you understanding?"

"Oh yea. She encourages me to ask questions."

"I have to say your English is so good!"

"Yours too… it is our first language?"

"Yes it is."

"Wait!" Shouts Canepiece-Rat in my direction, "Wait, the two a yu fegat everybody else bout ya?"

"Everybody jus a chat star! Wha wrong?"

"Everybody else a mingle!"

Hear how my girl just cold up the whole of them: "Although you guys are all having a good time, are you

telling me you can't be satisfied with my three friends?
He's over here talking to just me, you guys!"

"Me agree wid yu star!" Ackee Red pipes in,
"Is like the man fegat where him come from."

"A dat me a show you star, a dat me a say sah."

"Cho Po. Hunnu leff the people dem mek them
chat if them want chat."

A brief silence washes over the rock stones
before my interrogator continues.

"So you don't talk patois like your friends?"

"Who me? Me talk my patois when me ready
man but you know what I find! Whenever I meet
someone of the opposite sex for the first time, my
speech tends to be proper but as time goes on and I get
to know them a little more, it becomes easier. You'll
see... we become closer friends."

"Oh, you sound so sure of yourself!"

"I am. Yu watch we will start talkin more patois."

"But you yourself are like that, you speak better."

"Yea better pot watah, do you?"

"Every chance I get."

"You never did tell me your name?"

"Youtman."

"That's unique?"

"My uncle gave me... short for youth of a man."

"I figured that.... But you are different!"

Chapter Eighteen

TEX TAKES DABLO, THE FAMILY'S DONKEY, to the river for a drink of water. Thinking that my growth curve will still allow me to be a jockey I figure today is as good as any to start preparing for Dada's dream. I ask: "Tex! Beg yu a ride off of the donkey no man?"

"Yu can ride Jackass."

"No must."

"Take oath."

"A joke, me never ride yet but it look so easy…"

3333

33

"Well all right, if you think so."

I climb aboard from atop the retention wall. Dablo descends the path I sit leaning backwards to remain in the saddle, when he bends his neck further to quench his thirst; I am in awe of his brute strength. Satiated, he raises his head and Tex gives me the reins and slope climbing instructions. Ackee Red and Canepiece-Rat spot me. Things are going well when, unbeknownst to me, Ackee Red silently borrows Tex's whip and gives Dablo a swift one on the rump. The acceleration takes me by surprise and I fall backwards into the river on my coccyx and cut my right elbow and leg on the rocks. I am too frightened to be angry and too weak from the pain to fight and too wet to be hot under the collar and my buttocks hurt too much for me to even plot vengeance. Every detail of the traumatic event is permanently etched in my long term memory.

I return to Duncans and when I sit my Common Entrance Examination an instruction states that I write a composition; the Dablo incident is the topic of my composition. I may have done well on the preceding sections; but I know that I excel here. Passing eases my family's financial responsibility as all Jamaicans passing this exam are awarded different levels of financial assistance. Blessed with a good understanding of things taught, retention skills and the ability to later regurgitate same in my own words and at the comprehension level of my audience is a plus. I have no idea where this will take me but we a go somewhere.

We play jax with girls and steal glances when they innocently butu-down in an unladylike manner. We walk them to and from the shops, the post office, good news class, errands, escort them through shortcuts, wait by the river when we know they are going to bathe, follow them to spring for drinking water, we forget fear, lay in wait in the dark for them to make a pit toilet run. Our hormones are now on a full race lace focus. The girls smell the rat. But fearing isolation more than murderations there's usually acquiesce. But Marva, the God fearing 'grease-can' refuses to even acknowledge catcalls: "Hi, hi, dreamboat!" She pretends not to hear the caller: "Not you shipwrecked!"

Coded messages are set up: after a pebble falls on your roof, two shakes of a bottle torch, three winks of a penlight-- go to the toilet after night bus passes...

*   *   *

A new consciousness pervades our cleanliness
We join the bigger boys focus on their tidyness
As we go to the river to bathe and carouse
Parties meander to predetermined rendezvous

A new set of dalliance dynamics is beginning

317

Terrence R. E. Burey

Serious pairing
The rhythm of conversation has but one purpose
Acquiescence from the damsel under focus
As dusk envelopes us
Couples indulge in serious hocus-pocus
Trampoozing is a girl hunting art
And beyond district borders is the reckless part

It means endangerment of one's life and limb
As folks detest interests in their next of kin
In adjoining districts with demographic similarities
Boys share whoremongering dictums frivolities

The girls are certainly not whores
But boys paint such pictures by the scores
Making us all senior conquistadors
With higher than average damsel encounters

Boys claim to get more than John read 'bout
For passing girls, we lay'wait like scout
Press them to see what we can get shakin'
Then relate blow by blow in graphic detailin'

Enhancing our harem management database
We move on at a blistering pace
In desperate times batteries are run

A clique lines up each waits his turn at the fun

Were beefs (girls) not so maliciously maligned
Mothers could relax, remain less chagrined
But the female's treatment is the local addiction
Trapped by trackless mountains and misdirection

With nothing but time to kill
As young bucks we will
Do our best to kill the beef
In seeking some form of relief

As we get older we emulate the older chaps
Set our sights on the up and coming crops
A mission that replaces more than one hobby
Sure as the sun rises, for more we will lobby

We treat it in a plethora of ways
As wide as our fertile imaginations, always
Conjuring up new conjugation procedure
Every youtman thinks he is a master
And of girls as the bait

The girls are standing on their morals
Are beginning to rebuff our hardest trials
It started with just a few speaking up

Terrence R. E. Burey

Now it seems them de pon top
Here for example
Is the latest sample
See you boys
With all your ploys

Coming around holding our hands
Detaining us from our errands with your plans
It's time we put an end
To the pattern you contend
Stop having your children
So you can show off to your brethren
We must remain steadfast
Make acquiescence to you a thing of the past

Resist when you are forceful
Deny you reasons to be boastful
It is our future with which you play
Our hopes and dreams on the line you lay

So again I say
My answer is still no, come what may
For those of you without shame
We will deny you the personal fame

To the molesters of the young

Tell the courts and stand strong
It is high time we pursue careers
To come out of garments pockmarked with tears

To transact business without fear of a chance
You will stab at our dignities and call it romance
To the men of our district
Your appetites we suggest you constrict
Focus the attention on your wives
Allow us girls to have normal lives
The unwanted pressure you bring to bear
The difficulty you pose we walk home in fear
It is downright dangerous to be out after dusk
As you trail our scent as if it were musk

Our mothers before us suffered the same fate
Such fears our daughters need not contemplate
With a good education as societal alliance
We can put an end to your petty dalliance

Don't you have better ways to use your time
Than molest your own callin the process sublime
That is ridiculous
Our mothers need be more contentious

So much is stuffed in the closets with brine

It is no wonder our morals are on a decline
Time spent in solitary spousal remorse
It's something none of us need to endorse

Forcing us to be a part of something incestuous
We should deny the cover up, upend their status
Make them walk around delirious
Cause society to make them something hilarious

And so young women I beg
Brush them off like you would a forty leg
When they come you declare you are unready
You are waiting until you meet your own steady

*   *   *

Free Hill Daisy; certified teacher discourses with cosmetologist, Rosie. Daisy: "With these men 'No' does not always mean 'no' you know."

"A know… the next day when he brags."
"And gets debriefed by his comrades yu mean!"
"Yes, and tells them everything… bloomin chat."
"The bloody ego-tripping boy."
"Yea, that puts another stripe on his lapel."
"He and his friends should all go to hell."
"Yes me dear, fo' getting her knocked up."
"Missis. Have her 'a push dung bread van."
"A carry belly fo' him!".

"Knowing the consequences that she will face."

"Mr. Irresponsible still rides bare back."

"Drive barefoot."

"Without the Willy Penny."

"Reckless and willy nilly."

"Dem b'woys are good bad."

"Nothing change, nothing strange."

"What apply here can happen anywhere."

"Because the whole place set up same way."

"Yes hard times locally are hard times nationally."

"The thing is if he waits until he is older…"

"And still wants a child…"

"With her."

"If he waits… she will…"

"His fool fool act can cause a near loss of life!"

"Especially when grandmother-to-be finds out!"

"And tries to kill her for disobedience."

"As to them parent conflicting speech!"

"Smooth me dear!"

"Yu can say that again!"

"Yes me dear."

"Girls with puny rebuttals don't stand a chance."

"Like Princess!"

"She was like cheese to chalk in excess."

"I hear the boy roll out rebuttals to her denials!"

"Yes, stop only when him think him gone clear."

"What's that?"

"Forced agreement."

"Or whatever they interpret as being such."

"They bold… contradict a mother's directive."

"Like road signs…"

"Can you imagine!"

"Missis!"

"Bastards can hold their hormones in check…"

"How you know?"

"At times they focus on the hard nuts to crack."

"And border on belligerence to get acquiescence."

"Dish out promises… of love and affection…"

"On the primal night things come to bump."

"When a couple months later she tells him…"

"Declares the circumstantial evidence to conniving bastard, she will be looked at squarely in the face and asked: 'Yu tell the father yet?'"

* * *

Barby Thunder, Witnesses, cannot wait to drop the bundle of wood to share the news with his friend Bessie-Jumper-Sailor-Side-walker-Mackerel-joe from over Davis: "Froggy a overstep him boundary you know."

"Wha mek you say so?"

"Bwoy me see him a chat up chat Hyacinth!"

"My girlfriend! Oh, a so it go."

"Bwoy me couldn't believe me eye them."

"That's awright, a going to lay wait old master."

Froggy crosses the border and proceeds with his clandestine link up with Hyacinth. Bessie Jumper sailor side walker mackerel-joe jumps out of the star apple tree and accost the man over the wayward girl. They attempt to kill each other over her. Why. News of the altercation make the circuit, Ackee Red wonders aloud: "If that was me get caught with Forehead from Peckham, do I want to be a valiant fool or healthy coward?"

Canepiece Rat: "Me rather be healthy coward any day."

"Me too, stick it to the local beefs. Take my chance with a stray-way cousin, ha ha ha ha ha."

"Who we a kid… we soon broke out like them."

"You no know what them say?"

"What that?"

"Cousin and cousin boil good soup."

*   *   *

We learn by osmosis, from our mostly illiterate adults who find the best use for the newspaper at the ejection end of digestion.

The news and weather mongers flock to the tailor shop punctually, on the hour Jamaica time, thirty minutes late to get caught up on the broadcast news. Some may argue that they're thirty minutes early. As diligently as they come one would think they're learning something. Based on the far away look in their eyes, however, it's plain to see the information is still skating over their heads.

With eyes and ears peeled, speculative countenances interspersed within a sea of nods seem to follow the newscasts from beginning to end. Local commentators must be quelled so all can appreciate, as best they can, the hearing of the news. Through the commercials and as the announcer segues into the weather report, nobody's ears can eat grass. That everybody has an opinion, has a ring of truth around here as all that ails the country could seemingly be fixed lickety split by just about any of the parochial school dropouts gathered around the radio.

The weather report starts. Seriously speculative countenances interspersed with nods seem to concur with incomprehensible jargon. Still, they seemingly follow the weather report from beginning to end.

The weatherman,
>   The wind is out of the east at 'R'
>   And gusting to 'A',
>   Chance of showers at 'S'
>   The percent in the southeast diminishing to 'T'
>   Ridge of high pressure that's stationary over 'A',

There is a depression at latitude 'F'
And longitude 'A'
Two hundred miles east southeast of 'R'
Moving northwest with expected landfall at 'I'

Following the soliloquy, Dada releases an emphatic hhhmm hmmm as all the glazed eyes remain riveted to the radio, still listening, not knowing enough to know it's ended, not understanding one bit of what has just been said to RASTAFARI. Those Weathermen definitely did not hail from these parts.

* * *

Our closing school prayer rings true as it specifically begs to, 'Lighten our darkness;' we can certainly use a little of that. Not to be outdone by any parson or any radio, the wandering soapbox orators, the Warner Man, in an effort to stay fresh in our minds, ambles through the district with 'winter on his mouth' (froth; a sign of hunger) projecting bedlam. Frothy mouthed, he shouts of impending lightening, thunder, brimstone, pestilence, fire and floods. With his last warning fading from memory, the thatch gets dry; hot sparks fly. A wayward spark, a wayward kiss of the thatch and by the time you say 'a wha' dis?' Label it conflagration. Likewise, excessive rainfall in a catchment area and any river and its tributaries will, eventually, make the soothsayer's proclamation non-contestable. His correctness hinges on the fact that human memory fades over time. One's potential to forget exactly what is said when unless one is speaking of an important, perhaps traumatic event. A One, especially a righteous One, attesting to an impossibility: an undocumented, unimpeachable memory will step up and swear blind as to his accuracy and state that he remembers when and where he was, what he was doing and whom with, at the psychological moment the Warner man predicted that said climatic events would occur. And lo and behold, they have occurred. All praises to Allah. The man of God, the soothmeister now slides with non-contested backetive into the permanent retention area of one and all. Now he is established in all that hath ears, long term memory. And forthwith he hops onto the, "He told us so," bandwagon.

*　*　*

My friends and I spent our early years seeing things at ground level so the only place to move is up. Stoosh, high society lifestyles are too far up the aspiration chain to even be dreamed of. Big man's sons and daughters with the appropriate names are guaranteed a prepaid education, proper elocution and penmanship. They read and succeed; the proper channels, schools and direction are available. Finishing schools are pre-selected, acceptance through nepotism guaranteed. Lickity split they are welcomed on the society scene as doctor dis and doctor dat, mistress dis and mistress dat. News of these happenings reach us from our guardians who receive the news by osmosis from Buckra cook. Our parents hope that through this sharing better will come. Better mus' come. A private cadre is apparently at work ensuring that poor man-children remain unexposed to even the idea that there is a better life.

*   *   *

Shenanigans come to life at the end of the day the minute Massa's representative is out of sight and backs straighten. For most, the day ends then but for others it is a new beginning. It is from this narrow strain maintained cross-section that today's race took shape. From this multiracial beginning that our motto, "Out of Many one people" took shape. As an evolution perhaps the more apt, "One Big Rock One Melting Pot" should be adopted. Emancipation has rewarded us with, among other things, freedom to travel beyond the confines of Buckra's Plantation. Land Barons, by edicts of the courts, generously disbursed the lands taken from the Spanish who took it from the Indians and gave it to miscegenating Bushas and Buckras. As time rolled on, the 'controlled lan'' began to be divvied up in pie slices to those chosen few with whom Backra has personal dealings and who in addition to wet nursing him pickney with Buckrette also nursed their own half-breeds. Farming brought us here and it's still the main legacy from the slave masters. With successively subdivided crown lands, my countrymen did what they know best, grow bananas, breadfruit, citrus, coffee, plantains, sugar cane and yams. Soil chemistry facilitated region specific diversification of crops. This is the only way the black man knows to use to turn manpower into a quasi fortune utilizing the land to its full potential. Being smart in school is not considered a valid reason for refusing to help one's father in the field. One would be considered a smart-ass to do that. One may struggle to keep up for a while. Studying by the kerosene lamp or the kitchen bitch. Working harder, getting behinder. Should one's presence on the farm result in an abundant harvest, one might have just signed one's dropout letter to send to teacher.

* * *

With the exception of those working off o' missis clock', most all the remainder of the district gear their work cycles off the sun --an overcast day causes utter chaos.

Chapter Nineteen

FOR MANY GIRLS, THE SCHOOL WEEK ENDS on Thursday, Wednesday if the girl's mother is real serious about her higglering. As the main sustenance of any family, Marketing is a Thursday through Saturday event. Like the boys helping their fathers on the farms, girls help their mothers with the Higglering, the beginning of a glass ceiling. Sisters don't go on to much else 'cause they don't know much else. In time, sisters adapt to giving more than they get, in factors of ten. Repeated, cycles lead to better lives. The avalanche has started and we cannot be stopped. Those of us in the right place at the right time (which can be any place but here,) are training to become lawyers, doctors and various chiefs. A work, becomes a job, becomes a career; more can be helped. Passport possession is the new song of freedom.

*   *   *

The Bush Dackta's lack of local representation does not deny those with the belief, the will to leave on an early bus or hire a car to go to places strategically located, higher up the mountainside in the direction of Nine Turns or towards Wait A Bit or lastly, towards Gimme-Me-Bit. Flags fly high. It is in such locations that many people seem to decide their fate while paying questionable individuals with sums of cash and the carte blanche temporary use of their offsprings bodies that result in permanent mental scars. The adage says, 'belief kills and belief cures'; killin could result from these arrangements.

The citified folks in Kingston or other cities, with more exposure to life's offerings, are able to add an extra leg to the relay of life much sooner than the country bumpkins.

On Friday evenings we listen to Teen Age Dance Party on the radio. It's our way of keeping up with the latest music and hearing some of the hottest lyrics.

Rev. is good at setting up the radio so that we get the best reception. When T.A.D.P. is about to start, he places the radio atop his personally stored piece of Celotex and we take up residence at strategic points around the shop where we each believe is the best listening point on earth. We believe there is no deeper bass to be heard anywhere. We imagine, more than feel the exaggerated sound pulsate through our bodies. Its output of ten watts hit hard.

*   *   *

Monday evening is prayer meeting for all the keepers of The Faith. Tuesday evening is good news class, an excuse for young boys to lay in wait for ropable girls. Wednesday is washday and the big river is transformed into the laundress Mecca. Washerwomen with backs in semi-permanent arches, ache all day, in response to the manual labour postures, in positions God did not intend their frames and soft tissue to sustain. In the water rippling over the small rocks just above Longwater's misleading placidity and deceptive undertow Mahmus, Mama's laundress spends her day in the boiling sun. Others spend their day under the bridge; swinging the clapper above big river stones, perform a stress test on the fabric caught in-between while evidence of their energetic style ricochet off its cement underside. Two strokes of the quarter bar of brown soap, a splash of water and the washer ladies with their clapper begin the bastardisation-attempt to shred the clothes. They pound the daylights out of cotton shirts, khaki pants, seamstress-designed dresses and flour-bag undergarments, as well as drip dry. Rubberised delicates and elastic undergarments lose their intimate soils in the saw cuts to the scrisp-scrip-scrips of water, and soapsuds permeate the air through the lubricated fingers of expertly clenched fists. Not all washerwomen are created equal. And those bent on saving the clothing from becoming tomorrow's rags clutch a scrubbing board and coerce the dirt out of the laundry. Meanwhile their un-weaned offsprings bask nearby in bulrush settings, but unlike Moses, they occupy the riverbank as opposed to the river and are watched by baby-sitters thrice their age.

Thursday's downstream washing of a different kind: The hog, cow and goat belly, rid of their excrement is meat to complement the ground provisions for dinner of many who cannot afford to buy hind quarters, shoulder briskets or rump roasts. Others upstream and downstream repeat the process, but the overall populace is still solely dependent on the multipurpose river for drinking water and experience tests of intestinal fortitude when they drink too soon, the water the sand and aeration with insufficient cycle time fail to cleanse. Diarrhoea.

* * *

Death and dying are taken very seriously here in that apart from ones demise and obvious absence from the physical scene, it brings to the fore, the question of one's spirit. The district remains abuzz with reference to the recent absence but mention is seldom made to death without the use of its exclusive precursor, 'untimely': "But wat a untimely det him meet eh sah?"

Though pastor loves to berate the point through verbal citations, hymnal incantations and rhetorical innuendoes, he never fails to fall short of advocating that: since we are dying to meet Him, then dying should be viewed as a happening thing.

At an early age I learn that it is best to stay close to the embankment before a four or six wheel grim reaper: the car, robot, taxi, bus, truck can launch me into the air. The relatively high rate of speed at which automobiles 'burn the oil' through here almost guarantees that should one make contact with their bumpers, grilles, fenders and windshields, then, in keeping with the warp speed replay of one's life in great detail, in an instant, while the earthly body is being mutilated and without feeling the physical pain one is, as it were, transformed into a third party observer and experience the carnage as an out of body experience; one will have only a very brief time in the land of the conscious, to "Remember thou Thy Creator…" as, in the next instant… out goes the light.

Once the spirit leaves the body, friends and foe view the cadaver in a different light. Like parson, we agree that that has been reduced to whatever we are schooled to think the reduction needs to be called presently. But the one thing that does not change, is the feeling we have about the spiritual side of the deceased earthly body. We are more concerned about one's ghost. The duppy. We prefer that loved ones gone, stay gone.

Privately, measures are taken to ensure that a deceased loved one remains as such. Gone. Hist'ry. So, in death's aftermath, at the funeral, Parson takes over: "You know goodly people, it is at my discretion, that we will discuss the damnation of this male non-believer. As you all know! I may be short in stature! But I am never short! When it comes to denouncing Lucifer! I am never short! When it comes to displaying de exuberance of my bombastic vivacity! Let me seize this opportunity presented by the absented victim, especially one suddenly robbed of his youth, more so through seizure than by request! Because as hard as life are in these parts! Neither young nor old! Rich or poor! Is in the habit of requesting death! Of seeking out! Death! Of this puttykilla victim, he met a hot death. But I caution one and all through this alter call about your relative proximity to de hotter claps. De fire, and de brimstone!"

And so after extolling the virtues of the next to devil in hell at his feet; after placing the devil right up there with the righteous and giving all the community leaders and family members willing to say good about the bad, the opportunity to sin themselves right along with him, those who want to render a solo, a duet or a quartet or a whatever, a chance to render, he then makes sure to caution one and all 'bout their relative proximity to the hotter claps.

He tries saving as many souls as possible. Pre, during and post burial most older heads wax philosophic on the frailties of life. "But what is man? It is not too late for you within the sound of my voice, to save your soul through Chris'! Because in the twinkling of an eye! Like the great Magician! Abracadabra! Any of you, like young Gladstone here, can be turned into a hot cadaver..."

"But what is man?" Another fails to remain vertical the same unanswerable question is always asked: "But what is man?"

* * *

337

I readjust. We sit the exam. I treat it like a normal quiz with the exception of the portion that asks that I write a composition. As good as I am with the other subjects writing is a passion.

The topic of choice is left to us and so I choose something traumatic, which even without the natural ability of recall stays fresh in one's memory just because of its significance. The stimulant in the question takes me back to my Grandma's house, Tex, Dablo and my incurred wounds. My chosen topic: "My First Ride On A Donkey." It is written sequentially.

When the results are published in the newspaper, I am awarded a full scholarship to Middlesex College. I am attending school but for what reason? To tek book. Tek book and do what. Hit somebody?

Notwithstanding, the news of my success forces my proud father to seek a transfer so that I can live with his established family and he can vicariously enjoy beating whitey at his game by having me attend the same school to which he was refused acceptance. Excited, I visit my mother, now a practicing midwife in Essex Hall: "Sister Jasmine"

"I've tired to tell I am not your sister?"

"You don't have to tell me maam, I know…"

"So why you keep calling me sister…"

"Because I already call your mother Mama."

"I'd prefer if you call me mummy allright…"

"Yes Sister Jasmine…"

With a sigh she asks: "What is your question?"

"What does a midwife do?"

"Mama didn't tell you!"

"She said you can explain it better."

"I provide care to mothers and pregnant women."

"To a big area?"

"It's large… about three miles in every direction and as you see it is very hilly."

I make new friends, get into trouble, have a breadfruit fight, plaster the walls of her home with the boiled pegs and pay for 'roast and boil' with my rump when she returns home to find the house a mess. I am so mad with her for spanking me that I try sleeping at the edge of the bed. I turn sometime during the night. I am awakened by a distant sounding thud; the sound of my knee hitting the tile floor; and the resultant pain. The sound awakens my angry but loving mother: "What's the matter, with you?"

"Me drop off the bed maam."

Coddling me she asks: "Did you hurt yourself son?"

"Yes Mummy."

"Where you hurt?"

"Me knee Mummy…"

I return to Mama and Dada. Soon she and I are off to Kingston on my fourth residential move, to my third 'family'. Before joining my father and his family, we visit her long-time friends of days past in downtown Kingston. My godmother now lives off Upper Elliston Road and one of my mother's schoolmates, now married with a family of her own, is living on Range Crescent. We visit them both and spend a couple of days with each before going uptown to Barbican, where we join my father and his family.

Shortly before we leave I meet Prophet, the local visionary; she has the coveted adoration of everyone and interprets a dream I had. People from far and near diligently seek her wisdom as well. Prophet interprets my dream and tells of my success, "Once you migrate me son, the sky is the limit fe you, but if you stay here you could end like Perlie boy. You end won't be pretty."

* * *

Nationally, society rewards the lighter castes with jobs at the bank, the Post Office, as Cashier at the supermarket, the Librarian or The Paymaster. In the metropolitan areas, they man the offices as bosses and sexytaries. My kind takes out the trash; fetches the water; gathers wood for cooking; becomes a maid here, a day's worker there; cleans floors here; be a washer lady hither, iron clothes yon'; a watchman, a policeman and a sideman on a truck or bus. Begin apprenticeship as a tailor, a carpenter, a mechanic, sawyer man or shoemaker. Nothing mind you, that is too big to threaten our baboon brain into thinking its got to think. Nothing requiring anything beyond early miseducation.

Nothing hints at what absorption of secondary and post secondary education holds in store for the persistent pupil of all races, if only all races can get the break. The academics in the cities don't make it their business to spread the word this far except when passing through, even then, their code of conduct only permits them to swap words with the rum-heads who lay-wait them in the bars. Those among the subservient sufferers, who, on instinct, head off to the cities and with the added exposure begin considering: But me have to get an education… there has to be a better way… that things don't have to stay so... Nutten never have fe go so. Similarly, young women in the city, finding employment in the home of a high colour Doctor or Lawyer incite progress into the minds of their siblings or eventual, half breed children: Opportunity a lay wait we between the covers of textbooks! We must seek higher learnin!

But even before we get into these places of higher learning, some of us are politely kicked off the doorsteps of ethnic-centric secondary schools.

Almost made the grade student: They accept me at the school but a can't go!

"Why!"

"The school fee too high!"

"As you father a can't make school fee stop you."

"But is not only that Papa."

"Then a what."

"Me need money to buy blazer, broach, tie, khaki, shoes, socks, book bag and books!"

"Except the books who need all that to learn!"

* * *

I settle in and start secondary school.

"Good morning students"

"Good morning sir"

"As your principal it is my pleasure to welcome you to school...to you new students and transfers I'll have you know I personally went over your applications... many of your surnames I recognize... from the who's who columns of this island and others in the Caribbean... as you can see... our standards have shifted somewhat... a few names don't ring any bells... but so be it... I have no choice in the matter...

my opinion does not count for much in that arena... it does count however... for those of you that I consider... unable to cut the mustard.... Now for a brief history of the place you are about to do your matriculation... and not to worry... for those of you who remain here long enough... though it is not taught as coursework... you will know it before you leave... you may wonder why... I'll answer that with two statements... the first applies only to this morning's rhetorical question about the school's history...as you look around you... you will notice that both the upper and lower schools are represented here... everyone hears this address at the beginning of each and every school year, as long as you are privileged to remain here. The school was started in Saint Catherine and ultimately ended up at this location.

The second portion of my statement... Can you hear me in the black? I mean back?

"Yes sir," comes back as a rumble.

"Very good... for those of you who had fathers here... they, and their fathers before them... they followed instructions... to follow in their footsteps... so will you...of course this applies to a certain class of you but regardless ehehhhmm, regarding administrative directives, there is but one answer.... Yours not to wonder why... yours is just to do or die... is that clear?

343

Terrence R. E. Burey

"Yes sir."

"Very good. Until recently tuition fees allowed this place to cater only to the who's who… kept the ill affording away from the portals… they were none the wiser but… some of your fathers have seen fit to have the government offer free place to some of you… you who could not grace the cattle trap at the gates under normal circumstances.

The founding fathers have assigned a Latin motto to this English speaking school… where Patois, the country's second language is not to be spoken… to the Latin motto I say how eloquent… in the event anyone from Latin America, a Spanish and Portuguese speaking continent, comes over they will feel right at home. Now that you have seen my fun side… off you go, you sons of the red corpuscle bluebloods, get educated, shoot for the stars so that when you leave here, like your fathers before you, well most of you anyway, you can continue to be the leaders of our local and hopefully one day, our global community.

Because of constitutional restraints, you will be unable to become political leaders in our larger neighbouring countries, but in all other walks of life, the sky is the limit. In closing let me say this, it is my intention never to see any of you on a one-on-one in my office because when I do it is never pleasant… for me or for you… because you are sent there as a last resort for discipline… especially those of you who commute by public transport, do not attempt to use that system as an excuse for bad grades or report… at the end of the year if you fail to advance to the next grade you'll have one chance… to repeat the syllabus… should you fail, the following year you'll be taking a different bus… do your best, ace every test and as a school be an example for the rest…. Okay! Have a good year."

Terrence R. E. Burey

Glossary

a mawnin	tomorrow morning
awright	alright
back-han'-i'	back hand it
backle	bottle
bankin	banking, embankment
battie, batty	bottom , butt
bench and batty	close
bird speed	fast
bruk	break
brownin'	of brown complexion
Butu-down	stoop
caah me go	carrying me to
caan	cannot
chop him ten	cross his legs
cock say 'gi'me me draws'	early morning
cotching	staying at an inconvenience
cottered	cloth spiral twised cushion
cratch	scratch
bwoy	boy
dash way	throw away
dat	that
de	the
deggae deggae	single
dis	this
drap	drop
dunzi	money
dweet	do it

een ya	in here
f	if
fambly	family
fe	to
fegat	forget
fe yu pupa one gat cyar	your father alone has a car
fr'en	friend
fresh	facetious
gaa	go to
gallang	continue, go along
greendelero	body odour
grip	suitcase
gwine	going to
have sister visit from Red Hills'	see their periods
har	her
heinie	bottom , butt
hol	hold
humman	woman
hunnu	all of you
Johncrow	vulture
jubbies	love-struck girls
jus	just
Kerrnatian	Coronation
kitchen bitch	hand held kerosene lamp
ledder	ladder
lick 'im	hit him
ly	Lilly or Little
macka	prickle
madda	mother
Massa Gad	The Lord

Massy me pupa	Have mercy my father
mawnin	morning
membah	remember
Meeysuehunnu	I'll see you guys
naw	not, will not
needle-case	Spanish-needle
no do	do not do anything
nough	many
nuff	many
nuh	don't
Numbady	no one
nutten	nothing
nyam	eat
offa	off of
panya jar	Spanish jar
parochial	narrow-minded
pee pee	urinate
pee pee bed pickney	bed wetting child
pitayta pone	potato pudding
pon	on, upon
pork	white man
quattie	a penny and a half
raise	get, are sent
rahtid cup	darn it
round a tunnin	around the corner
sah, sar	sir
sake-a-how	because
school a kip	school's in session
s'ite	saw it
sitten fe teef	something to thief

349

SNAFU	situation normal all f----d up
testin	testing
thread hens	probe rectally for eggs
tump	thump, punch, hit
wan lickle twep	a small portion
Whappy kill Phillop'	a long time ago
washa humman	washer woman
ya, yah, yasso	here
Y'ear	You hear
Yeye	eye
yu	you
yu a foo fah	to whom do you belong
yuself	yourself

ABOUT THE AUTHOR

Terrence Burey received his formal education in Jamaica at Frankfield Comprehensive High School (now Edwin Allen High School), Jamaica College, The College of Arts Science and Technology (now University of Technology) and in The United States at Tuskegee Institute (now Tuskegee University).

While obtaining his education, he held a variety of jobs including being a mechanic, cab driver, driving instructor and an accountant. Burey is a mechanical engineer who spent twenty years in the computer industry. He lives in Florida and visits Jamaica frequently.